In the beginning

was the Word

and so shall it be again,

and the Word

is the Law,

and the Law

is Love.

A Leaders of the Way book

In the same series

The Way of Love
Recorded Channellings

Compiled by Peter Wheeler

THE MEMORIES OF JOSEPHES

The Soul Memories of a Cousin of Jesus

David Davidson

Series editor: Peter Wheeler.
Copy editor: Judith Timmins.
Cover illustration by Christopher Greene.

Published by The Leaders Partnership.
P.O. Box 16457, London, SE14 5WH
ISBN No. 0 9532007 0 1

LP and the star design are trade
marks of The Leaders Partnership.

First edition 1997. Printed in the UK
by Redwood Books, 23 Bedford Square,
London WC1B 3HH
Set in 11 on 14 point Galliard.

for Japeth

'On Cyprus there were places of great healing power. When we were boys we would seek them out, not intentionally but we were drawn to them. They were places of intense beauty, where the leaves of trees would reach down and provide gentle shade over mossy banks, where the air was always fresh and cool. We would talk in whispers as we paused and rested in them and nature would talk back, the breeze in the trees singing softly, the gentle trickling of water – there was always water in those places, a natural spring or just an abundance of moisture. That summer we did not need a temple to be in the presence of God; God was all around us, in every leaf and stone, in the sound of the sea and the air. We needed no rabbi to remind us to be reverent; we walked in innocence, hushed by the sanctuary of nature.

'And when one of our expeditions was over we would return to the house tired and hungry, our feet sore from walking and our skin burned from the sun. Then there would be Miriam waiting, wanting to know of our adventures and we would tell her a little but give up when words could not capture our feelings. It didn't matter, she could always tell and she would listen with her head to one side and her eyes would fill with love. Then the blessing of nature would give way to the blessing of family. There can be little to compare with the feeling of fulfilment, with the pleasure in our simple food when we returned from one of these trips.

'After we had eaten we would join the company of the family together, curled up on a rug or couch, and we would drift into our slumbers, the murmur of the adults' voices gently around us, and sleep peacefully and deeply into the next long day.'

Yeshua, Summer 1996

The Memories of Josephes

How this book came to be written

The first Leaders of the Way book, 'The Way of Love', sets out the truth about Jesus the Man and Jesus the Christ from a Jewish viewpoint. These revelations, through a deep-trance medium,* are by Joseph of Arimathea who was an uncle of Jesus and masterminded his education as a young man. In that book the story of the Master Christ is revealed, much of it through the past lives of people living today, together with the Essenic teachings which so strongly influenced Christ's own message – the Teachings of The Way.

One of those past lives of 2000 years ago was the life of Josephes, the first-born son of Joseph of Arimathea. Today another aspect of his soul lives in David Davidson (not his real name), an Englishman living in London. David found that during the period 1993 to 1996 he could actually recall many events which took place during that life in Palestine. In meditation he found that he could see and feel as if he were Josephes himself. These episodes would remain fresh in his mind long afterwards, like fragments of a powerful dream, so he started to write them down. This book collates those memories and gives a vivid insight into what it was like to be born and brought up 2000 years ago under Roman occupation. More significantly, since Josephes was the cousin and constant boyhood companion of Jesus (Yeshua), it also gives an intimate and human picture of the life of Christ, his family and his teachings.

*Note: The deep-trance medium referred to above has been channelling for the past 20 years but it was not until 1987 that the identity of the speaker was revealed as Joseph of Arimathea (the Biblical figure reported in all four Gospels as the one who obtained the body of Jesus after the crucifixion). However he prefers to continue to be called simply the Master, for he is the spokesman for a group of souls and therefore uses the sum of their collective memories. In this book therefore any reference to the Master is to the Arimathean and those souls that assist him.

Josephes' family.

Josephes' father was Joseph of Arimathea, a teacher in the Temple and an Elder in the Sanhedrin. His mother was Miriam, the daughter of a wealthy merchant. They were a very rich family for Joseph had been born into the privileged class of the day. His father was a wealthy man, the owner of a successful family business selling tin, timber and acting as a middleman importing silks from India and from China.

Joseph of Arimathea was very well educated in the Jewish faith. He had at least a working knowledge of several other religions and had been to India in his youth. He was also versed in several languages, (he could write and speak Greek, Aramaic and Hebrew). His own father wanted him, as the elder son, to devote his time exclusively to the family business but he wanted to be a rabbi and teach in the Temple.

On the death of his father Joseph inherited not only the business but the magnificent family house in Arimathea, a home on the island of Cyprus (where he was a great landowner), and property in Greece. Cyprus was used as a holiday home by the Arimathean family and the family of Jesus; it later became the home of Josephes when he married. Although Cyprus was ruled by the Romans, there was no occupying army and it was an extremely beautiful place, quiet and peaceful. Later, using among other materials magnificent hard woods imported from his Cyprus estate Joseph of Arimathea built a house next to Golgotha in Jerusalem. This he used while working in the Temple, for it was too far to travel from Arimathea.

While still young he fulfilled his boyhood ambition by becoming a rabbi, an Elder in the Sanhedrin – the ruling body of the Jewish faith in Jerusalem – and a teacher and counsellor in the Temple. He enjoyed fine clothes and particularly bright colours and dressed opulently, especially compared to other rabbis.

While working in the Temple he entered into a relationship with a woman by whom he had a daughter, Mary

Magdalene. This knowledge was hidden from his family for many years.

The father of Jesus was old and Joseph of Arimathea had to assume the role of parent to his nephew. Joseph supplemented his education with special lessons, took him to Egypt and masterminded his long stay in India – probably the most important part of Jesus' spiritual education. Then on the death of Joseph the Carpenter the Arimathean became the guardian of his mother Mary. Like Jesus, the Arimathean family were all direct descendants in the line of King David.

So this was the family into which Josephes was born. He was the eldest son, and so was expected to take on the responsibilities of his father. He had an older sister, Rachel, and a younger brother called Eliazar. Jesus, known to the family as Yeshua, was Josephes' cousin and was his companion, closest personal friend and confidant from a very early age. Josephes was born in January, a Capricorn, and Yeshua was born in the sign of Virgo a year and a half later, so Josephes was the elder by twenty months. Both John the Baptist and Simon Peter were also cousins of Yeshua and Josephes.

The genealogical charts at the end of this book (taken from 'The Way of Love') set out the relationships within the immediate family, relationships which, in the text of this volume, are imbued with all the depth of human suffering, joy and triumph.

Peter Wheeler, Series Editor

Chapter 1

Josephes walks into the sea

A constriction in my throat, sadness or grief, but I cannot let go to the tears. Grey pyramid-shaped rocks. It is evening and the light has almost gone. I have come here to be alone. My grief turns to numbness as the moon rises. I am aware of the water lapping against the rocks. I am in the small bay near the family home on Cyprus; the bay that was the scene of so much lightheartedness and joy in childhood is now companion to my grief.

I have just heard news of the crucifixion. My cousin is dead. The man I loved more than any other has been killed on the cross. I can accept the words but not what they mean. The feelings come in waves, and each time the tears come I clench my fists in rage. If my tears are spilt I will have to accept that it is true.

There will be no sleep for me tonight, no sleep and no comfort until I have made my way to Jerusalem to find out for myself.

I have just arrived in Jerusalem from Cyprus. I am talking with Simon, a Nubian servant of the household with whom I grew up. I have never seen him like this, so shocked, so readily moved to tears. He is explaining to me the events that have taken place over the last weeks, those things that led to the death of my cousin on Golgotha. He tells of the trial, of my father's absence, of the scourging and humiliation of Yeshua and of how helpless he was to stop the course of events. He talks of the terrible feelings that all who were present suffered, of the darkening of the sky and the rolling thunder. He tells of the scattering of the disciples and supporters now gone into hiding or denying that they ever knew him.

Together we examine the empty tomb; some claim to have seen him but Simon does not believe them. He watched Yeshua die. Simon looks to me for help, for my father is nowhere to be found, but my feelings are numb, my eyes are vacant. Since I cannot share his tears, anger fills the void where grief should be.

My family and I are on the shore of the Sea of Galilee. It was my idea to come here, where so often we came with Yeshua. He loved this place. In my longing I have convinced myself that perhaps he will come again, I will see him again as I did on the road. If he were to come at all I know that it would be here. So we wait and we walk.

My feelings cannot be reconciled: rage, hope, despair, grief. They take turns to tear at my insides. It is a terrible thing to realise that without him there is not enough left in life to make me want to go on.

He will not come. I know that I am just putting off the inevitable. When I met him on the road after the crucifixion it was not just gratitude I saw in his eyes, it was a farewell. And now I must accept that he is gone...

I am looking into the eyes of my son*. This one is special, he has my eyes, my father's eyes, the eyes of Yeshua, as blue as the sky. He is looking back at me. His eyes are steady, there is no trace of fear in them.

In my arms is my son, in my heart is grief. Grief and anger. I wonder if he can feel it pressed so close against my chest. I feel the cold waters of the Sea of Galilee around my legs, cool and cleansing, cleansing the pain in my heart. He does not even flinch as his body touches the water, but I hold him tighter anyway.

In my secret dreams I wanted to give him to Yeshua. So that he could share what I shared, so that he could learn from him. Yeshua loved this one; he loved children so much and they knew it and loved him back. And now he is gone.

The water closes over our heads.

*14-month-old Japheth.

I am looking back over my life in contemplation. There is so much time here, time and space and help to understand. I see the events that led me to this, events that ultimately caused me to ascribe so little value to my life that I was prepared to turn my back on it and end it by my own hand. I am beginning to understand now more clearly the purpose of my life, why I was so intimately involved with these two great men – my cousin and my father – and of the covenant that brought me here at this time. I am thinking about why I was so often subject to correction by the authorities when I was younger. So many times I claimed what was not mine to claim by right, what I had not earned: power, authority, opinions. So often I looked outward to the gifts of others, and sought to emulate them rather than looking within at my own gifts.

One of the tasks I undertook for this life was to learn love, and I was given all I needed to learn it: a life, a blank sheet of paper upon which to write.

My father gave me wealth and freedom and my cousin gave me example. I certainly used all the opportunities that were afforded me. Love is a hard lesson to learn, it cannot be learned without humility and humility is not learned by walking the straight path; it is learned more through trespass than obedience to rules. Now I have broken the final rule, I have to accept that having ended my life whilst in the midst of such learning means that I am now unable to harvest the fruits and apply them to my life and my actions.

But the fruits will not go to waste. Such fruit that I have not put to use will be harvested later, by another.

✡

These memories were amongst the most poignant and vivid of all the memories of that time of 2000 years ago and were to arise several times in David's mind.

It may initially be hard to comprehend why a man of such wealth and good fortune should be driven to take his own life and that of his infant son. In this book David

Davidson sets out the details of Josephes' everyday life, as a youth and then as an adult, and tells us of a beautiful younger cousin, a companion he loved more than life itself. Here David presents a very human side to the story of Christ: intense love, fierce anger, misgivings and doubts as well as profound loyalty. In these writings we learn of what led up to that momentous time when Josephes learnt in despair that Yeshua, his cousin, had been crucified like a common criminal.

Peter Wheeler

Chapter 2

Earliest memories

A memory of my birth, of the circumstances surrounding it. An absolute but non-verbal understanding of why and with whom, of the timing, the parents, the point in history being critical, nothing left to chance.

The complete and utter loss of perspective, the consuming claustrophobia of the body, the clarity being so muted and muffled by the cacophony of light and sound and discomfort. Then through the noise and confusion the points of recognition and communication: the eyes, they speak without recourse to language. In my mother's eyes I see that I am in the right place at the right time and in my father's eyes I see why.

Becoming aware.
Bright sunlight and severe shadows, not too long so I guess it to be just after or just before noon. It is extremely hot. I am very small and my attention is taken up with the intensity of the light, the colours, the textures and the contrasts. The ground is baked earth, a pinkish colour. There are many people here. I am with my mother. I think that this is a very early memory of being outside the home.

Joseph of Arimathea.
It is dark. I am under blankets. It is freezing outside. The night sky is black and the stars are brilliant. I am in the desert but I am not alone.

Someone sits close by, their back to me; a man, I can hear his voice, chanting softly, perhaps praying. I can see his breath misty in the starlight. He is a devout man, he seems a little stiff and formal. He leans over to check on me, his hand gentle on my shoulder and he sighs and turns back to the night, to the silence. I hear his breath, I listen to him breathing, wondering what he is thinking about. He seems sad, as if there is a burden on his shoulders.

I awaken at dawn, crawl into his arms, my body

warming his, and he holds me as the sun comes up. I have the impression that he has been awake all night. I am about two or three years old. He is my father; he is a good man, his responsibilities are great and he has his eyes on something far away that I cannot see.

Miriam, Josephes' mother.
We are laughing uncontrollably. I am with my mother, she calls me her little Josie. We laugh a lot when we are together. She loves to make things from clay, she models heads and people and she is very good at it. I sit with her in her room helping her mix the clay and roll it out so she can press it on to what she is making. Sometimes I make things myself and she keeps them; she has a shelf full of the things that I have made for her.

The flight from Herod.
A white wall; the corner of a house with the sun shining upon it. The ground at the bottom of the wall is a sandy ochre colour. I am alone, about three or four years old, perhaps a little older. I am bored. A hand on my shoulder – it is a man, my father. He is young, lean, muscular and tanned. He talks to me, straightening my hair and tunic as he does so.

He is telling me something about a trip, a journey. At first I think that he is going to leave me behind for he has often been away on business before and always I have stayed at home. This time I realise he is going to take me with him, we shall be going together. It will be a long journey on horses and with camels and helpers to carry the supplies. It will be an adventure and Yeshua will be coming too. He explains that the place we will be going to has tombs called Pyramids and he draws one in the sand for me to see.

The journey to Egypt.
The courtyard of a large home. It is the house where my father grew up. The hills are barren and yellow, the roofs

are tiled in green and the yard is dusty and dry. It is a large house, more of a complex. I am very small, playing with some pebbles in the dust in the yard. There are many people here, servants, many of the family, my mother and father and many children too. Everything is happening quickly, there are people hurrying, calling and shouting to each other and packing things up. We are going to live in another country.

I am riding a horse. It is my father's horse and I am sitting on the saddle in front of him. We have been riding all day and we shall be riding again tomorrow. It is a long journey. Sometimes I ride with my father and sometimes with an older cousin, the youngest of Yeshua's elder brothers. He is a young man of a happy and kind disposition who is often put in charge of the younger boys; he takes great care of us, always ensuring that we are looked after.

There is quite a procession of people and camels, which are used to carry the possessions, and horses on which the people ride. My mother and sister are far back in the party and on occasion I ride along with them. It is by no means an easy journey, there is the heat, the dust and always the smell of the animals. The adults say we are in danger but riding on my father's horse and between his arms I feel little fear, only adventure.

Meeting Father.
I make my way across the marketplace. We have settled now in Egypt and many of the people there know me and call my name as I pass but I do not have time to stop and talk with them, I have my eyes on a corner on the opposite side of the square to our house. The building is made of a similar material to our house, a light pinkish stone although it is stained with age and the passage of people. There is an alley that leads off to the left where the corner is and I turn down it into the cool and shade between two buildings. The alley issues on to an open sunny courtyard surrounded by buildings. From here it is just possible to

see the distant mountains enveloped in a hazy blue mist.

The courtyard is fairly busy with people passing to and fro but I am waiting for someone in particular. I can see him now, coming up the hill. He smiles as he sees me and I run to him. He lifts me up and I ride on my father's shoulders back through the marketplace to our house. I must be somewhere between four and five years old.

On the banks of the Nile.

An arch of dense and verdant foliage and beyond an immense and sparkling river. The sky is blue, the air full of bird song and laughter. We have reached this place by boats which are moored in the shallow waters of this cove.

The whole family is here and we have come here for an outing to escape the noise and pollution of the city. There is food and wine in baskets carried in the boats. Amongst the party are members of the family with whom we are staying and their servants; we are in Egypt and this river is the Nile. What makes this scene so special is not just the extreme beauty of the place but the atmosphere that is created by so many of the family being gathered in one place at the same time.

Shrieking children playing in the shallows, the conversation and laughter of the adults and overall the most intense feeling of wellbeing; no past, no future, just being in the here and now.

Playing on the seashore.

Water, a river or perhaps the sea; children are laughing and playing in the shallows. There are some women here, charged with responsibility for us, sitting on the bank talking whilst they look out on the playing below. It is a happy time, we are quite young, naked, perhaps three and five years old and I am digging in the soft earth and mud. I am absorbed with this activity and so is my cousin. I build the mounds and decorate them with pebbles and then he pushes them over; it seems to be a very co-operative relationship.

We run into the water to clean our hands and bodies, then to the women; they are elegant and indulgent, and wrap us up in dry linen cloth. We wander off along the grassy bank looking at the plants and pebbles. I can recall no sense of anything other than a natural appreciation of what we see, the colours are bright and vivid.

There comes a man along the path, he is tall and dressed in a brown toga with blue cloth over his head, he is my father. He squats to talk with us and joins in our observation of the bits and pieces we are examining. He tells us the names of the plants and asks us about the pebbles, and we tell him about the colours. He picks us up, one in each arm and carries us along the path talking to us. I can see his face clearly, he has kind eyes, dark skin and a black beard. It feels good to have a ride in his arms as he laughs and joins in our chatter.

Early travels with Father.
Yellow flames, a fire in the night. We are outside in the desert. The fire is carefully tended for wood is scarce and fuel must be carried. I am in a tent, quite young, sitting beside my father. He is in conversation with a large bearded man who owns the tent we are in; I think that he is an Arab, a desert dweller. My father and he are obviously very fond of one another. To my right sits Yeshua, we are both cross-legged. The attention of the large man falls on us when there is a lull in the conversation, he refers to us as the 'two fine boys' and winks at us a lot.

Singing a Jewish folk song.
I am sitting with my arm around Yeshua's waist. His left arm is across my back with his hand on my shoulder. We are quite young, of nursery age I would guess, or perhaps a little older. We are in a group of other children of a similar age, singing and rocking from side to side in time with the rhythm of the music. We are singing a beautiful Jewish folk song that is a favourite of us all. The class is being led by one of my father's servants, who is banging a

small drum in time with the music, grinning as he enunciates the words for us to follow. It is a charming and happy memory of the simple joys and innocence of childhood.

Near the Pyramids.
I can see the Pyramids shimmering in the distance. I am sitting on some rocks looking at them. This is another family outing and we have come here for this purpose, to view the Pyramids. We will not be travelling all the way out to them today but my father says that we will go sometime soon. I am very young and I am part of quite a large family group that includes my sister, Yeshua and one of his elder stepbrothers who is looking after us. There is quite a bond between myself, Yeshua and this elder brother. To us he seems almost adult; I think that he is only seven or eight years older than us, but when you are so young seven years is a lifetime. He is more fun, more accessible than the adults and although strict, makes us laugh a lot.

In a tomb.
I am looking at a very old wall. There is no light save that of an oil lantern that my companion is carrying which illuminates a small area of hieroglyphs; we are discussing the meaning of them. We are here by very special dispensation, it is a very ancient and holy place, the existence of which is kept secret from all but a few. We have all had to vow that we will never reveal its presence to anyone. Yeshua has gone on ahead to the very deepest part of the tomb with my father in order that he can read some very special scrolls. I am here with a young Egyptian man, an Essene whose community guards the secrets of this place. I like him, he is kind and funny in the way he explains the pictures on the walls, quite irreverent in fact.

We hear the voices of Yeshua and my father approaching from the other end of the vault before we see the lights. With them is an older man with white hair and beard. They come directly to where we are standing. The older man nods to my companion and says something to him in Egyptian, then looks down at Yeshua and smiles. Together we begin to make our way out towards the exit passage when there is a deep rumble from behind us. A light breeze touches our faces and causes the lantern flames to flicker. My father hurries us along and looks at the older man. It is the younger of the two who addresses himself to Yeshua, 'So you are the one, and the last for some time to have sight of those scrolls I think.'

Yeshua does not speak of his experience in the tomb. It seems to me that it had far more significance to the adults than it did to him. When I ask him about it he explains that my father told him that it did not matter whether he could understand what was presented to him, but that there were important secrets. If he looked at them they would remain in his memory until he would need them and then he would understand them better. Then he says, 'They were mostly pictures anyway.'

Thinking of the past.
I am standing in the ruins of a city. Great yellow stone blocks and arches lie toppled into a chaotic jumble, eroded by the wind and choked by the sand. We are quite young, a few small children standing in the ancient remains of a great civilisation. We listen obediently as Father talks of the ways of people who lived here and of their beliefs. He has us close our eyes and imagine the broad streets and avenues as they were, full of people and buildings, palm trees and the shouting of children.

He tells us how every great civilisation has great knowledge and understanding and of the learning that the Egyptians had at the height of their power. He tells us of their religious rites and practices and of the golden sun disc which they worshipped.

A healing.
A cat, a young tabby cat sitting on the branch of a tree just above our heads. There are many cats in the cities of Egypt, mostly wild but some are kept as pets. We are

21

trying to tempt this one down from the tree in order to play with it. The cat is quite alert and is watching Yeshua's capering and gesturing quite intently, although it shows no sign of vacating its perch.

Finally Yeshua gets down on all fours and starts trailing a twig with one dried leaf attached to it on the ground. The cat immediately becomes fully alert and finding the twig irresistible jumps to the ground. Instead of landing as we had expected with the grace and beauty for which cats are renowned, this one lands in an untidy bundle and lets out a yowl of pain. The twig now quite forgotten, the cat looks disconcerted and confused. As it stands up the reason for its distress becomes apparent for its right foreleg is quite lame.

I cannot exactly say how the next thing happens but without hesitation Yeshua reaches forward and grasps the afflicted leg in his hand. It happens in an instant, for as quickly as he holds it, he lets go and casually leans back, sitting on the floor to watch the cat limp off painfully toward the safety of some bushes. As it walks its stride becomes more confident and it allows more weight on to the leg until by the time it is twenty paces from us, it is walking almost normally. Then as if it suddenly realises that the pain is now gone it pauses, looks back towards us quizzically for a moment and then disappears from sight. Yeshua looks over to me, pulls a face and we both burst into laughter.

Yeshua has a brother.
A dog barking in the middle of the afternoon, the streets are deserted, the air is still. Two small boys are sitting in the shade of a house. It is Yeshua's house, his mother is inside, she is having a baby. My mother is there, too, to help her, and we are waiting outside. We are both listening attentively, we can hear the sounds of the labour, it takes a long time. The cry of a baby then another wait. A servant comes and calls us inside. It is cool and dark inside the house. The adults are pleased to see us and make a fuss of

us. Yeshua goes straight to the side of his mother and I am beside him. She holds up the baby for us to see, we are captivated by him, he is so small and perfect. She tells Yeshua that he has a brother and me that I have another cousin. There is a closeness between us, an understanding, almost as if in this moment we all are one.

Contemplating early education.
I am lying on my back in long grass, arms behind my head, looking up at the blue sky. I am chewing a piece of grass, screwing up my eyes and watching the patterns the light of the sun makes as it refracts through my eyelashes. Next to me is Yeshua, he is lying on his front, his head propped on his elbows. Both of us are wearing short white tunics, are barefoot and are about seven or eight years old. I say that my father has told me that when we return I will have to go to the Temple to learn the Torah. My cousin replies that it is because we are Jews. I reply in a defiant and humorous way that I am not a Jew, I am a boy. He rolls on to his back and looks at the sky; in a slightly puzzled voice he replies that he really doesn't know who he is.

Life after death.
A tower, unusual stone buildings and architecture, chanting in the distance. We have been in Egypt for some time but I am still quite young, with a party that includes my father and cousin. Our host is a local man who has great knowledge of the ancient teachings of the Egyptians. We are at a temple or tomb of some sort and he is explaining to us the meaning of the hieroglyphics that are carved in the stone at the entrance.

We enter. It is cool, dark and dry inside; as we progress the sandy floor gives way to paving. Deep inside there is an anti-chamber. I am very struck by the carving of two birds standing face to face that adorns the lintel above the door to the main chamber. Our host pauses and explains the significance but my attention is drawn to the walls which are covered with pictograms; Yeshua's attention is also taken by these. We proceed through the door to the main room, where there is a sarcophagus, richly decorated in gold and a most beautiful deep blue. Our host explains that this is the sarcophagus of a great spiritual teacher and that the pictures on the walls tell the story of his life and of his teachings. My father questions us at certain points in the dissertation to ensure that we have understood what the man is saying.

Much is made of the fact that life is a continuum and that at death there is a change rather than an end and that we live time and time again in a different form. I try to imagine what life after death is like and content myself with the thought that whatever this life may be, the after-life will probably be like the sarcophagus and that we, too, will be covered in blue and gold. We are thoughtful when we leave the tomb and stepping into the sunlight is like walking into a wall of heat. Although we had entered quite early in the morning it is now past midday and we must have been inside for many hours.

A timeless moment.
I can see my father, seated in a chair made of oak with draperies on it. We are gathered at his feet, five or six children and young people sitting cross-legged, a huddle of skinny arms and legs and knees and elbows, all of us looking up at him. Amongst us is my brother and sister, Yeshua and two cousins. My father is telling us a story from the teachings. We are in the Jerusalem home so it must be after our return from Egypt. He speaks with warmth and humour, stopping to answer questions or clarify points as he goes. I look over his shoulder; the light at the window is brilliant, there is a cool breeze coming in through it and my mind wanders out, imagining the people and places he speaks of. Hardly knowing it, I slip into a reverie of timeless security, absorbed in the moment, embraced by my father's voice, by my friends, my family and the tradition of my people.

Visit to a disused temple.
A very large temple. It is not a Jewish temple but is more in an eastern style with a domed roof and minarets. I am walking towards it. Along the sides of the path are wild flowers with tiny vivid blue blooms. I am with a party of others and we are visiting the temple because of its historical importance. I have the impression that although the temple is not in ruins neither is it in use. We draw closer and it is clear that it retains a holy presence; the walls are adorned with beautiful and intricate calligraphy. The doors are missing and there is nothing inside save the dry dusty floor and the flapping of the wings of some doves who have made their nests in the dome.

Our guide is explaining the significance of the building but my attention is drawn to the beautiful scale and proportion of the architecture. It is not unusual for my father to arrange trips such as this or to make quite long diversions to historical sites when we are travelling together. He has a deep interest in all things religious and takes great care to broaden our education in this respect.

Playing near the Temple.
Sun-baked steps. They are the steps outside the Temple in Jerusalem and we are sitting on them, two quite young boys. There are many denominations represented here and their representatives are coming to and fro in the costume of their faith. Some are plain, some are forbidding and some are colourful and fancy but none pay any attention to us as they pass.

For our part we are absorbed in playing a game like five-stones, throwing pebbles in the air a short distance and catching as many as we can on the back of the same hand. When we tire of the game we run off across the road, dodging the traffic of people and beasts. We are barefoot and each one of us is wearing a white tunic which is more or less the way that all children dress, some with an additional robe or headcloth but most prefer to be unencumbered by such things unless they are out with their parents.

We arrive breathless at a friend's workshop in an alley near to the Temple. He is an old man who works for Yeshua's father. He does not work with the others but has his own shop where he carves particularly intricate designs for the furniture. He is always pleased to see us and although we always treat him with respect he always treats us as equals. We stay and talk with him for a while and watch him deftly carve the wood stopping each few moments to freshen the edge of his chisel on a whetstone. Before long we are off again tearing down the alley to some new destination.

Joseph of Arimathea.

A cup, a rather beautiful cup, made of pewter with stones inset. It is being held by my father who has an amethyst ring on his finger. He is dressed beautifully in silks of purple and gold. He is thoughtful and poised as he drinks, his other hand flat on the table top. He takes his position and the wellbeing of those who depend on him very seriously. He is the head of the family and unlike many others leads in as even-handed and fair way as he can. It is not just an accident of birth and marriage that has put him in the position he is in, he is possessed of wisdom, wealth and authority. I love him very much and feel glad to be his son.

An initiation.*

I can see my father's right hand, clenched into a fist. He is sitting leaning over a table and is in great pain. The clothing has been removed from his back and my mother is tending to the deep weals that are left from being beaten. He winces as she touches them. It is confusing to me, my father seems to have subjected himself to this treatment voluntarily, as part of his progress at the Temple but it is still hard for me to understand why his examination should involve his being beaten.

* The Master was asked about this very unusual memory and whether it was true. He replied, "Part of the doctrine of the Jewish faith did at

Images at bedtime.

An oil lamp. Three or four are gathered around it, their faces illuminated by the light of the flame. We are gazing into the flame and talking in whispers so as not to disturb it. We are quite young, and I have the impression that Eli and Yeshua are here. We take turns describing what we see. I say that I can see gold, Eli says that he can see sunshine and another says that he can see the sands of the desert. There are long silences between each utterance and each is concentrating his imagination into the light. It is a kind of game we play at night.

Childhood mischief.

White-washed houses with thick walls. Jerusalem. The street has some chickens in it. I am in an animal pen which is part of one of the houses and which opens on to the street. It is dark and cool inside the pen while the outside is brightly sunlit. Others are in the pen, adults gathered to watch the procession. A rabbi approaches slowly in the lead holding some sort of staff. I watch closely, absorbed by the whole thing. As the rabbi draws abreast someone pinches me quite hard, I let out a yelp, the rabbi scowls. Exploding with mirth behind me is Yeshua. He is so full of irreverent mischief, no thing is more sacred than another to him. As soon as the procession is past I turn to chase him, ducking under the elbows of those who are watching.

one time contain an element of scourging. As far as we are aware this practice has been discontinued although in smaller sects in Jewish communities in some eastern countries such practices may well continue. Certain questions would be asked of those entering the Sanhedrin or synagogues as rabbis and if the responses were not as decreed by the learned ones – those steeped in the mysticism of the truth as revealed by Moses – then a rope would be brought down on the bare flesh of the back. The idea was that those that were sincere in their desire to move forward in the teachings should study every aspect of Jewish Law and be proficient in explaining it. Very little licence was allowed to those who could not remember or considered that any part of the law need not be strictly adhered to. The back of Joseph of Arimathea was lashed three times during his initiation and we feel it is this incident that has evoked the memory that you describe."

Chapter 3

Growing up

There is a rope hung from the branch of a tree on the side of a slope. We are six or seven quite young boys, we are playing a game where first one swings out on the rope then, as he swings back toward the others waiting on the bank, another jumps on to the rope. At each swing another body is added to the collection until the whole company are hanging on to the rope and to each other like dates on a palm.

The game always seems to have the same ending: after the last boy has mounted, the rope eventually comes to a halt and the only way off is down. The second half of the game consists of each member trying to pull each other member off the rope as they fall, and usually ends up with an untidy bundle of fighting boys scuffling on the ground under the rope.

Yeshua joins in with as much enthusiasm as everyone but when things get rough I am ever aware of him. He is not particularly strong in his body, slim, fine boned and gentle which has occasionally earned him the scorn of other children. It seldom comes to anything though, partly because I am one of the strongest in the group and often the leader. They know that if they harm Yeshua they will have me to reckon with. There have been confrontations in the past but now it is unspoken, they understand the situation.

Sharing.
We are sitting on a dried bank of grass. I am eating a piece of fruit. I eat with gusto at first and then more carefully and then in tiny nibbles until I have eaten exactly half. I pass the uneaten half to Yeshua who accepts and eats it. No word is spoken; half each, that is the way that it is.

A cruel act.
We are on the bank by the olive tree from which hangs

the rope but on this occasion we are alone. Down the bank in front of us there is a dusty path and then the stained white wall of a house. There are no other children about and we are sitting panting in the shade of the tree, away from the sun. We do not speak, we are exhausted from running and still in shock for we are both deeply upset by what has just happened. In every town and village there are those who hate children; as children ourselves we do not question it, we simply accept it. It is of no comfort to us to know that those who hate do so because they have been hated in their turn.

Perhaps we should not have been where we were but our actions were motivated by curiosity, not mischief. We stole into a yard, attracted by the crying of kittens to look at the newly born and there we were found by the son of the owner, renowned for being as cruel as his father. At first he was decent towards us, picking up the kittens and asking us if we liked them, then he started to tease us, asking us whether we thought that they should live or die. He was obviously enjoying the effect he was having on us and enjoying his power. He chose the one we liked the best and asked us if we would like to keep it. We both said yes and then he squeezed the little cat in his hands, oblivious to its crying with pain and fear. He crushed the life out of it and tossed the pitiful little corpse toward us. We just ran, his guffaws echoing behind us.

Now we sit in shock. I can hear behind me Yeshua start to cry but I am more angry, plotting revenge. I hear Yeshua ask if the older boy will kill the other kittens. I reply that I do not know, perhaps the mother cat will take them away and protect them, but privately I think that he will destroy them all for he enjoys his power.

Helping in the kitchen.
In Cyprus; bread, the kneading of dough to make bread. I am helping the woman in the kitchen, a servant I think, not my mother. She is kind to me and teaches me how to cook. When we have finished making the loaves I wash my

hands and help to load the oven. The oven is fired by wood or charcoal and it is my job to watch the fire. When the bread is cooked we take it out of the oven and lay it out to cool. I like to help in the kitchen, especially when this woman is cooking, she is a favourite of mine.

Companionship.

Cyprus again; the table is laid with fruit, bread, olives, nuts and fish. Maybe eight or ten young people are gathered around, not sitting formally but after the prayers are said each of us going and taking what we need, then eating in our own time what we have chosen. There is talk and laughter and the teasing of the adults who are present, too.

Beach games.

A group of children, the eldest is about fourteen, the youngest can barely walk. All are naked or near naked and playing on the small beach near the villa in Cyprus. In and out of the water, laughing and yelling. There are adults, further back, sitting and talking. There is one young man who more or less takes charge of us. He lives in the vicinity and comes to visit when we are here. Yeshua is amongst the group, not in any special way, just playing along with the rest of us, shouting and laughing.

Looking after younger brother Eli.

It is summer, we are near the sea, making our way down to the beach. We have to clamber over rocks to make our way to the shore. I am with Eli who holds my hand on the difficult parts. He is about five years old so I imagine that I must be about nine or ten. I have mixed feelings towards him; I feel love, protectiveness and pride in him but there is also a little of the distance and tension that can exist between brothers.

There is a trust and innocence about him, he is extremely self-contained and demands little from the company he is with. He has a very independent kind of curiosity and sees things on the shore that others miss.

Like the rest of the family I am quite indulgent towards him but the tension springs from the feeling that there are demands on me that I suspect will never be put on him. Above all I feel an appreciation of his eccentricity. He has a way of looking at the world that is not quite impractical, it's just different in quite a beautiful and fragile way.

A philosophical discussion!
'There is something there!' Yeshua points down excitedly to a plant and we both squat down to examine it. It is green and leafy and there behind the stem is a small toad. Yeshua captures it and sets it on the back of his hand, cupping his other hand over it. We both stand up and examine our find through his fingers, Yeshua holding his wrist up at eye level. We squint into the toad's eyes and then set it back where he found it, behind the plant. A discussion develops about whether a toad is more stupid than a lizard since a lizard would never have allowed itself to get caught. The argument gets quite heated and we barge each other across the path as we walk, Yeshua taking the part of the toads and I the part of the lizards. We decide to ask Yeshua's father to resolve the argument since we are going to his home anyway.

We track down Yeshua's father and ask him our question and he replies that neither one is stupid, they are what they are and that is all. Joseph can be rather grumpy at times but still it is a puzzling answer to us and we go on our way trying to work out what he meant.

The power of love.
I am lying on my back looking up at the blue sky and sunlight through the leaves of a tree. Beside me is lying Yeshua. The tree is an olive and the fruit is ripe. We are lazily sucking some of the olives, they are green and cool in the mouth.

This is not a memory of actions but of atmosphere. The afternoon is lasting forever, there are few words spoken, it is a memory of the simplicity of friendship. There is usually so much to divert the attention but when everything is taken away – conversation, work, worries and activity – it is not nothing that is left; what remains here is love.

A secret place.
We are on the outskirts of Palestine, looking towards the city. There is a sandy-coloured haze hanging over it but out here in the low hills the air is clear and bright. We are walking and each of us carries a stick and a water skin. Barefoot, we are headed for a valley, a secret valley some miles away that has some trees for shade in the hot sun. We come here often to spend the day. As we walk we talk about everything that attracts our attention, the rocks, the cloud formations and the sparse vegetation.

We pass a dried-up gully and stop to dig and poke with our sticks in the bed. I find what I am looking for and pull out a piece of soft clay which I mould as we walk on. I enjoy modelling, like my mother, and Yeshua loves the little figures I produce. I make a fat Roman and we both laugh and leave him guarding a rock by the path with a twig for a spear.

As we approach the valley we become quieter for the little valley has a great peace and stillness to it. We talk softly as we approach. We find our trees, cypress I think, and pine, and sit in the shade looking out over the valley. We watch the lizards in the hot sun as we talk. There is a presence in the valley, and both of us feel at home here.

Yeshua champions a poor boy.
He is standing on a small hill. I cannot see over it. He beckons me to join him. On the other side of the hill there are a group of boys playing on the sun-baked earth between some houses. They are laughing and running, playing tag. I am not sure if we are to join the game or not but before we can an ugly scene develops: one of the boys, smaller and from his mode of dress poorer than the others becomes the object of the derision of the others. I have the impression that he is often scapegoated in this way.

Yeshua and I make our way towards the group and he intercedes on the small boy's behalf. He is firm, both angry and very still at the same time. He upbraids the bullies who then become angry with him, their eyes alight with hatred. I move in close beside him in preparation for a fist fight but none develops. There is an authority and clarity in Yeshua's voice as he speaks but his fearlessness makes me anxious. He talks of justice, of how none have the right to presume superiority over another. It is not just what he says but the way he says it that carries such impact. He says that they cannot know what is in the heart of another, nor what brings the younger boy to the position in life that he occupies. There is a tense moment before the bullies back down. Yeshua turns to the boy whose face is stained with dirt and tears. Yeshua puts his arm on his shoulder, no words pass between them but I see the boy's face soften as the fear leaves him and his eyes shine with the recognition he has received.

Yeshua contemplates his healing hands.
I see the sea, several small rocky islands, uninhabited, with grass on them but no trees, very close to the coast of Cyprus. We are on one such island with a small boat moored a little way out – we had to swim ashore.

Yeshua and I are sitting cross-legged on the grass and talking. We are discussing Yeshua's hands. He is aware that his hands have powers that are not shared by others but to him his ability is natural. He can restore life to insects, lizards and small animals with a touch and often those within the family who are not well are refreshed and lifted by his touch. He is curious about this power and we often talk about why it is and what it means.

An idyllic summer afternoon.
Two boys, in a small wooden boat, drifting on a warm, calm, sunny afternoon. So much of our time in Cyprus is spent in the sea or in small boats. We are talking idly, enjoying the lazy motion of the boat, enjoying one

another's company. It is such a blue sea, a blue sky, a time-less afternoon. An easy companionship and understanding exists between us; the silences are easy, the relationship is one of deep ease. And there is always the sea, the great blue sea. Fingers trail in the water, the sun is low in the sky, we will have to pull ashore soon but neither of us wants the afternoon to end. A line pulls, we catch a small fish but spare its life and put it back, laughing and asking the fish to forgive us.

We beach the boat and secure it and make our way up the steps to the house, tired from the hot sun and salt air.

An accident.
Yeshua and I are out for the day, excited and ready for adventure. We are in the shallow waters along the coast a short distance from the Cyprus villa. We have come here in our little boat, against the advice of the adults – not specif-ically on this occasion – but we have taken advantage of their confidence in us and have explored a little further than we would normally do. Yeshua is first out of the boat and I watch him carefully; being a little older the expecta-tion of care usually falls on me when we are alone together. The landing is difficult, there being quite a rocky and steep shore to negotiate. I am tying up the boat when I hear Yeshua call out. I clamber up the rocks and find him lying in a crevice between two large rocks, not particularly deep but quite sheer; he has clearly slipped and fallen down. When he sees me he calls up, 'Josephes, I am fallen.' I climb down and help him up, but as he stands it is clear that he is hurt, he has twisted his ankle and it will not support his weight.

With a little difficulty we get out from between the rocks and with my help Yeshua half-walks and half-hops back down toward the boat. Once we are safely back in the boat and heading for home my mind turns to the reception we are likely to get from the adults. They will know immedi-ately where we have been and what has happened; they are constantly warning us against that particular stretch of coast, for exactly the reasons that have come to pass. I look over at my cousin as I row. He seems unconcerned, both by his accident and by whatever pain he may be suffering as a result.

During the return journey Yeshua is quiet and I am pre-occupied with my thoughts. Now that the initial drama of the accident is over I will have to explain to the adults not only how it happened but even more difficult, why it was allowed to happen in the first place. I moor the boat at the little jetty by the villa and help Yeshua on to the shore. The first person we meet is one of Yeshua's elder brothers who demands to know immediately what has happened, so I provide the briefest of information – that he fell – and he is picked up and carried into the house.

I follow slowly behind. It is not so much the admonition of the adults that I fear but that of this particular cousin who can be quite austere in his judgment. Once Yeshua is delivered into the care of his mother the cousin turns to me and wants to know exactly what we were doing on that stretch of coast having been told time and time again that it is dangerous. Of course I am struck dumb by his ques-tions, we went there because it was forbidden, and this made it all the more exciting, but such thinking will hardly appeal to the logic of adults. My silence enrages my inter-rogator all the more and he starts to yell. It is only the intervention of Yeshua himself that stops what is rapidly turning into a full-scale attack, his thin voice cutting through the tirade: 'He pulled me out, he didn't push me in.' My elder cousin looks angrily over at Yeshua and says, 'Well you shouldn't have been there in the first place,' and stalks out of the room.

His words were not meant harshly, in fact he cares very deeply for his little stepbrother, and for me, too. Each male member of the family feels a responsibility to all, and as the oldest male in the situation he took it upon himself to play the role of the elder and admonish us. It is accepted, that is the way of the family.

Yeshua's wilfulness.

There is a deeper significance in Yeshua's older brother's anger. Yeshua is extremely wilful, he does only that which he wants to do and this creates tension in his family. All his brothers are trained in the profession of his father and take an active part in the family business, but not Yeshua. He dislikes physical labour and shows no interest at all in the work of his brothers.

He gets away with far more than they were allowed to and all attempts at discipline have failed. Although he is loved deeply by his family they fear for him and his behaviour can also give rise to frustration and resentment.

Josephes' intimate relationship with Yeshua.

Cool white cloth against my face, being pulled over my head: it is the sleeve of Yeshua's tunic. It is a hot day and we are alone on a hillside. We are dancing around each other in a rather ribald way, yelling and laughing. The cause of our merriment has something to do with sex, with women; we must be young adolescents and are letting off quite a lot of steam.

We fall panting on the grass; the grass is sharp and scorched pale yellow – it is perhaps midsummer – and there is joy and an anarchic exuberance in our capering. The talk becomes more earnest. We are both bound by the vows of our faith and those vows are strict, desire having no part in them. There seems to be a danger in discussing such topics and yet the talk brings an intimacy, a closeness that is worth the risk.

Yeshua heals a baby bird.

Walking barefoot along a sandy yellow path. There are green fields full of crops and orange groves, figs and apples. I think we are in Cyprus. We stop briefly to pick up apples that have fallen by the side of the road and eat them as we walk. We are making our way towards a low dwelling, the home of a neighbour and friend whose father grows the crops in this vicinity. There are two brothers, and the elder who works with his father is a favourite of ours; he has a sense of fun and adventure and is always indulgent with us. His young brother is the same age as us and our friend. There is a yard beside the house and the brothers are there helping to pack fruit into baskets. The baskets will be loaded on to donkeys and carried to the market for the next day. We all help sort the fruit, leaving aside the bruised or unripe.

When we have finished, our friend's brother calls us into a storage building. It is dark inside and he signals us to be quiet then he motions us forward and points to a nest built in the roof space. We can hear baby birds. He and his brother smile and look on as we climb up to peep inside. The mother bird has flown away and in the nest are two little chicks, a third is dead or dying. Yeshua reaches into the nest and lightly touches the third chick. It revives immediately; he looks up at me, grins and we climb down to the others.

A sympathetic ear.
I can feel the heat on the side of my face and hear the gentle Cyprus sea. I am walking alone with a heavy heart. I am aged about ten or twelve. I see Yeshua in a cove, squatting, looking down into a rock pool. I hadn't expected to meet him, I came here to be alone. He hears me coming, looks up and calls my name, then comes over to me.

He asks me where I have been and says that he came to find me, he knew I would be somewhere along this part of the coast as I often come here to be on my own. I am touched by him coming so far to look for me and by his cheerful concern. He senses my unhappiness and asks me what is the matter. I reply that my mother is sick again, she has taken to her bed, in pain, irrational and depressed. He listens carefully as I talk, he is always attentive when listening to my troubles. It helps to talk and I cheer up a bit; she has been through this sickness before and has come through all right.

At the Temple.
I am being handed an open scroll with writing on it. I am
at the Temple with my father. I spend a lot of time here
since our return from Egypt. The man who handed me the
scroll is tall and slim, dressed in deep turquoise silk. It is
Uncle Nicodemus. We call him uncle but my father says he
is not a real uncle. It doesn't matter to me, though; he is
very kind and patient and takes great delight in talking to
me. He asks me about my life, the things that I like doing
and I explain that I have always enjoyed baking bread. He
says that baking bread is very important and that bread is
the main part of what we eat. Then he says that there is a
story in the scroll about bread, a special kind of bread that
saved our ancestors from starvation when they came home
from Egypt. He opens the scroll at the part about the
bread and suggests I read out the story, stopping me to
embroider it as we go. There is something very special to
me about this uncle. I am always happy to see him, he
always seems happy to see me.

Cattle.
Oxen, standing between the walls of two buildings or
perhaps in a narrow lane. They are large beasts but docile.
Yeshua comes through them toward me, looking tiny
against their enormous sides. He is young, perhaps eleven
or twelve years old. We turn and make our way up the lane
away from them. We climb a hillside and sit on some rocks
to rest awhile and look back down the hill to the place that
we have left. It is a small settlement and the oxen have now
been led into a pen. Around the settlement is farming land,
not easy land to farm for it is hilly and rocky in places.
Seeing him beside the oxen has made me aware of the
gentleness and frailty of Yeshua; we are throwing stones
down the hillside and he cannot throw them as far as me.
Finally he makes a comical self-deprecating sound and
gives up trying. We laugh and he leans against me and puts
his head on my shoulder. It is a gesture that is typical of
him: he has never been shy of admitting his own insuffi-

ciencies or his need for love and his guilelessness and innocence in this respect make him enormously lovable.

In a strong friendship time and distance are of no importance.
I raise my eyes and am looking out over the city of
Jerusalem. We are about twelve years old, seated on the
ground in some hills on the outskirts of the city. There are
few tall buildings in the city, it being very largely made up
of one- or two-storey dwellings so my father's house and
Golgotha are clearly visible. I have a feeling that we may be
on the Mount of Olives. We often come to this place to sit
and talk when the heat and noise of the city is too intense.
Today is a rare day, for Yeshua's studies have been taking
him away more and more recently so we have been seeing
less of one another. It doesn't seem to matter too much
though; in a strong friendship time is of no importance.

We talk of school. Yeshua's studies take him to Qumran
while my own studies when in Jerusalem take place at the
Temple. Like Yeshua I have studied at Qumran and the
teachers are known to me. We talk in different languages,
trying out our knowledge with each other. He is more
comfortable in Aramaic whilst I am learning Greek. Within
the larger family we speak in Hebrew. We tell each other
about our teachers and are both keen observers of their
bad habits and inconsistencies. We talk also of the other
young people with whom we are learning. We are both
looking forward to the summer again which we will be
spending in Cyprus, but each of us is aware that the time
of our youth and our innocence is slipping away. We each
have responsibilities to take on and we know that such
responsibilities will separate us for long periods.

Josephes and Yeshua philosophise.
I see light, diffuse white light, as if I were lying under a
thin white sheet in the daylight. We are both lying in this
way. The sheet is a canopy of some sort and we are lying in
its shade. The canopy is erected on two sticks like a tent; I

think that it may be some of our clothing that we have used for this purpose. The sun is strong but there is a gentle breeze which cools the air in the shade. We are young, perhaps thirteen or fourteen years, and in Cyprus, quite a long way from the house.

A small bird lands at the entrance to our makeshift tent, and showing no fear, hops inside. We lie absolutely still, breathing very quietly, and watch as the little bird investigates the ground inside. It is delicate and fragile and we cannot move lest we frighten it away. Eventually it simply turns around and flies away. We both collapse and gulp down air, chattering about how incredible it was to be visited in such a way. A discussion develops in which we agree that the little bird must be like the touch of spirit, seeming so delicate, fragile and apparently without fear, living according to its own laws, and how we must be so still to allow it to visit.

And they knew him not.
A group of priests or scholars are filing in through a door. I can see the door and the porch quite vividly; the porch is a patchwork of stained yellowish stone and plaster and the door is of heavy oak, old and white, the grain opened with age. I am looking up at the priests so I assume that I am quite young, still a boy. Yeshua is beside me and he beckons me to follow him as he tags on behind the last in the line. There are six or seven of them inside, coughing, talking, shifting furniture noisily and moving around the room in preparation.

The room is an annexe to the main temple, the walls are bare and the furniture is heavy and dark. There is a menorah on a stand, also made of wood. It is made in the form of an arrow pointing up. Set in the wood are brass sconces for the candles. The centre sconce is on the point of the arrow with the remaining ones arranged down the two arms at equal spaces. There is room for seven candles in all. I have the impression that this room is open to the public at a certain time each day for those members of the community who may come with their troubles and questions to seek the help of those who are assembled.

Yeshua wastes no time in his questioning and asks why the Jews are the chosen people. The answers come quickly and in a variety of tones, from the patient and genuine to the downright patronising. The gist of the answer seems to be that one people must be closer to God, to guard His words and works from dilution by other religions. Yeshua asks why the Jews are deemed fit for this task, why not another religion. The priests respond by saying that Judaism is an ancient religion that cannot be separated from its people and that the traditions of the Jews ensure the purity of the lineage of teaching. Then, asks Yeshua, are you saying that the Jews are naturally closer to God? They answer in the negative saying that a Jew may stray from the path as easily as a Gentile but in the tradition of the Jews the word of God is strong.

Yeshua seems satisfied with the answers that are given and changes his tack slightly; he asks of the Messiah and whether the scholars expect him to be born of Jewish blood or not? They answer that it will be so for this is the way in which it is prophesied.

Some are beginning to tire of Yeshua's questions and others are becoming dismayed by their very precociousness but they continue to answer nonetheless. 'And if this son of God were to present himself in this temple, how would you know him?' he asks. 'By His beauty and by the power of his speech and his radiance, by these things all would know him,' they reply. And yet when the guardians of the word of God gaze upon him they know him not. How can you explain this? They look confused and uncomprehending, none of them can make the leap of belief that would be required for them to entertain the possibility that the boy standing before them might be the Messiah, I am not even certain that Yeshua himself can.

He does not press the point, nor does he reveal his own suspicions and so there is nothing for the scholars to refute, he just wants to know what they know; they fall to scholarly explanations about the coming of the Messiah.

Fooled by a lizard.
A lizard, quite a big one, darting into some rocks as we approach. It has left its tail sticking out. We are walking in the hills surrounding Jerusalem. We spend many hours in this way, sometimes stopping to observe some plant or the behaviour of an animal or insect for hours. On this occasion it is the lizard that has caught our attention. It is most unusual for a lizard to leave any part of itself showing when others approach and so we stop to see why this one has advertised its hiding place so obviously. We sit down on the path and wait for the lizard to move but it does not. Yeshua whispers that he thinks it must have died of fright when it realised that we were not going to go away.

Before long our patience wears thin and we gingerly approach the rocks. I reach down fully expecting the tail to disappear into the crack in the rocks as I draw near but instead I am able to pick it up. I rise with only the tail between my forefinger and thumb, the lizard is long gone. We both burst into laughter; we thought that we had the lizard fooled but it seems that all the while the little creature had fooled us.

Exploring a gorge.
I can see Yeshua's legs, he is sliding down the side of a big smooth rock towards me. We have found a rocky gorge with some deep clefts between the rocks which form almost cave-like gullies. I am at the bottom of this cleft and Yeshua is sliding down towards me using his heels to slow his descent. It is silent and cool between the rocks and we make our way deeper into the gully exploring.

There is nothing here save the atmosphere, nothing alive except perhaps for the odd snake or lizard but they generally prefer the sunshine. We make our way out, not the way we came but towards the wide end of the passage which opens on to the hillside lower down. Here there is evidence that the gorge has been used as a night shelter.

There is some burned wood in a comfortable part of the gorge not far from a smooth rock which would have made a good backrest for the occupant.

We try to imagine who camped here and how long ago and why they didn't go into Jerusalem which is not that far away. When we have finished we exit into the sunshine and continue on our way.

Fulfilling the expectations of their father.
I am looking at some of the beautiful things that are in our home: silk drapes, beautiful furniture and rugs from the east in many of the rooms. There are finely decorated boxes for personal possessions as well as clothes for special occasions and for daily wear. The family of the Arimathean are no strangers to wealth and those within the home want for nothing on a physical level.

Perhaps because of this the issues of status and individuality are more acute within the family. All are educated to a high degree and are aware of their privileges so it is important to each one at least to fulfil the expectations of the father if not surpass them.

Josephes and the family business.
I am travelling with my father, I spend a great deal of time with him now. It is the way amongst our people that the eldest son accompanies his father about his business. Sometimes, when he is conducting business with a friend he trusts who also has a son in my position both the men step back and allow their sons to conduct the business – at least that is the theory, more often they interject and point out where we are going wrong the whole time.

Then when we have struck a deal the men decide whether it was a good one or not and start the whole process over again between themselves. In this way the sons are trained in the business of their fathers and new bonds are formed that will ensure the prosperity of the families in the future.

A tea break.
I am sitting cross-legged on the ground, to my left is my father who is seated in a similar manner. Before us is a charcoal brazier and all the paraphernalia required for making hot tea; the cups are made of pewter, the kettle is tinned brass and the brazier is also made of brass. Tending the kettle is Abu, not particularly because he is the servant, it could just as easily be any one of us, but on this occasion it is him.

It has been a long and tiring day of travelling and we are all in a somewhat contemplative mood, quietly looking into the glowing coals and listening to the hiss of the dew as it drips from the outside of the kettle into the fire. It is not always possible to prepare a hot meal when we travel but always a hot drink is made, which brings a deeper nourishment and an inner warmth to set against the freezing desert nights. Above us the stars are so brilliantly arrayed that they would render insignificant anything that we might have to say to each other, so we say nothing.

A visit to Britain.
Pebbles. With water washing over them. We are on the sea shore, or to be more accurate at the mouth of a very broad river. The sea is grey and cool. I don't think that we are at home in Jerusalem, possibly we are in Egypt. I am standing with my father who is pointing out some boats that are moored in the river. Apart from his interests in minerals, silks and timber, my father is the owner of a large fleet of sailing vessels. There is one in particular rigged in the manner of an Arab dhow. He is speaking to me of a trip to a country called Britain where we have relatives who are rulers. He explains that they also have interests in mining and we will be going to negotiate the purchase of tin. He tells me that he plans to take both myself and Yeshua to accompany him. We will be sailing in a boat such as this one, a long and arduous sea passage that will necessitate coastal navigation around the land mass that is Greece, Spain and France. I am extremely excited about the

prospect and ask many questions about the details and where and with whom we will be staying.

I am angry. As the day for our trip has come closer it has transpired that Yeshua will be unable to accompany us and that I will be travelling with my father alone. It is an arrangement that is not to my liking at all, I would far rather stay at home with the family if my cousin is unable to come. I have been fairly outspoken with my protests and tears but my father's word is final in these matters and so to save my pride I have decided to put a brave face on it, but it is with a heavy heart that I now make the final preparations for leaving.

It is the day of departure and the whole family have assembled on the quay side. The boat is laden with chests tightly bound with waterproof cloth containing gifts for our hosts, goods for barter and all the things we will need for the journey. Yeshua is there too; he had as much desire to be a part of the trip as I had to be excused of it, but it has been decided that his time will be better spent in Jerusalem, so there are two rather resentful and angry boys to contend with on the dockside.

When all have embraced and said those things that people say to each other before setting off on long journeys I turn to join my father on the boat, for he is becoming impatient to leave.

Despite my pledges to myself and my father that I will control my emotions I cannot prevent my tears spilling over as I wave to my friends on the shore. My father's hand on my shoulder brings little comfort and I angrily shrug it off; at this moment I hate him.

It is a long time before my mind returns to the journey we have undertaken. It is a long way to go and my unwillingness to be involved in the venture at all makes every second of the first few days an hour long. The journey stretches interminably before us, it will be the furthest I have ever travelled from home and although I am used to the sea and to travelling by boat, I cannot even imagine the sheer length of time that travelling so far will take.

It is not too many days before our party's excitement at setting out together has given way to the introversion and discipline that is required to withstand the unrelenting exposure to one another in such a confined space. The boat is small and virtually without shelter so all personal habits must be performed in front of the other members of the crew. Several of those aboard are expert fishermen and much of the food we eat is culled from the sea around us; otherwise there are vegetables and preserves that we have brought with us sealed in clay jars. All of our food is eaten cold except when occasionally a small charcoal brazier is lit to prepare hot drinks.

There is a small cabin-like structure in the middle of the boat which provides more shade than protection from the elements and this is used for sleeping. Even though we are not a large party, numbering less than ten, it is my father's wish to make good speed so there are always several sleeping or resting in there so that they can pilot the boat when others take their turn to sleep.

The major pastime apart from those duties that are necessary for the maintenance of the boat and the feeding of the crew, is either talking or listening to the conversations of others. Since no part of the boat is out of earshot of any other I am able to learn a great deal from this activity. Once a day my father spends a period of time with me in pursuit of my studies and these times are generally conducted in Greek, which affords us a little privacy.

The method of navigation we are using is to sail in sight of the shore by day and by the stars at night, so our progress is measured by those recognisable landmarks that are visible on the shoreline. We are some way into our journey and I am leaning on the gunwale of the boat, gazing into the water as it slips by. Like me, many of the party have slipped into a silent reverie. We have been expecting sight of a landmark, a tower set on a hill, that will herald the opportunity of a port and a much needed break from life on the boat. There is a feeling that the tower that we are looking out for is long overdue, which probably reflects more the need for the break than the fact that we have been slow or missed our course. When there is finally a call of recognition from one of those who are watching out, there is an immediate commotion and craning of necks to glimpse the sight.

After a deal of consultation and opinions being exchanged it is agreed that the solitary tower, grey in the distance, is definitely the one we seek and the course of the boat is changed to find the small port at the base of the hill on which the tower stands.

Our stay with the community who offered us shelter for the night has been all too short, consisting of a simple feast and one night on dry land. It has served to refresh the spirits of the crew however, who despite the difficulties of the language hardly conversed with one another at all, pre-ferring the company of our hosts.

We are now aboard the boat once again and navigating the straits that will start our journey northwards. The seas change on the other side, darker, colder and less pre-dictable with strong onshore winds to contend with. As we progress it becomes clear to me that despite the monotony, the easiest part of our journey is behind us and from this point on we will have to work hard. There are times as we press on to our destination that the boat is lashed with wind and rain, times when the sea offers us little food and times when the sudden changes in weather give us cause to pray for our very lives.

It has been many months since we left the sun and light of our homeland behind us. Life aboard the boat has changed each one of us imperceptibly. Despite my age I have grad-ually become accepted as an equal member of the party, and my duties and the expectations of the crew reflect this change of status. Sometimes I feel that I have been on the sea for my whole life and that my family and friends are nothing more than a distant dream. My attitude towards my father has changed, too; he has seen the man emerging from the boy and has adopted a less protective and over-bearing attitude towards me.

A day or so ago we left the mainland and began the final haul to Britain. This last leg has so far been conducted in a fine drizzle of rain so it is a great relief to us all when the sky begins to break up and reveal in the distance the long low coastline ahead of us. We are beyond attempting to make more haste at the sight. Each one knows that but for the grace of God we would not have got this far and that that grace will also finally bring us to our destination. We quietly and patiently continue our tasks and wait until we have sighted port.

We enter a small natural cove which has a timber pier built out into the water. There are other small craft moored and a steep shingle beach. Beyond the beach is a path that leads to several simple dwellings. From the dwellings comes the sweet scent of wood smoke which drifts out across the water. There are one or two at work on the beach. One man stands and calls out to us. We cannot understand the language but my father calls back the name of the man with whom we will be staying. This seems to meet with some recognition and after a brief con-versation his companion sets off up the path while he himself boards a small boat to make our vessel fast and to ferry us to shore.

Our host whilst we are here is a relative of our house who is also a nobleman in this country. As we travel to his home I am struck by how different this place is to anything I have known before. The landscape is flat and marshy; it is damp, cold and appears to be without the benefit of too much sunlight. It seems to me to be a most unappealing place in which to live. Fortunately my feelings are lifted by the people we have met so far who have been warm, open and extremely hospitable.

Most of the homes are similar to those that we first saw at the harbour although some are more elaborate. They are constructed from things that are about us: namely timber and mud, the latter of which appears to be available in abundance. But the home of our host is singular; it is very large indeed compared to the others that we have seen. Built partly of stone it also comprises two storeys in certain parts. It is within a fenced compound with smaller buildings, presumably for servants, dotted around and making up part of the perimeter wall. Upon entering this house all my impressions of this country are challenged completely. In total contrast to the environment around us it is full of the most wonderful atmosphere of warmth, intimacy and comfort. There are fires burning, animal skins strewn on the floor and on the furniture, children running, family, servants and dogs all living in close proximity to one another. I thought that I knew what homeliness was but the people of this island have taken the art to another level entirely.

The master of the house, when he appears to greet us, is a most remarkable man. The King of this region stands in the large hall of his house with his arms open in welcome. Surrounded by his family he greets and embraces us one by one. He is of medium build with very dark brown eyes, black curls to his shoulders and fully bearded. I immediately feel both safe and assured in his company. Like us he is a Jew and speaks Hebrew. When he has made us all welcome he presents his family to us: his wife, his sons and their wives, (for he is older than my own father), and his daughter to whom I take an immediate liking. He expresses his hope that her command of Hebrew will improve through our relationship. Although I do not know it now, despite being several years older than I, she will become a firm friend and a source of understanding during our stay here.

Despite our tiredness there is a great deal of talking and drinking that goes on late into the night. For the first time in months I am able to watch my father from a distance. It is good to see his pleasure in talking to one who despite being of a different country, is a peer. I watch the way things are done in the house, the attitude of the servants and the family to one another, the harmony between the members of the household, and conclude that this is a house that is similar to our own, for each one is afforded respect and courtesy whatever their station may be. It must have been such thoughts as these that accompanied me to sleep for my next conscious recognition is of it being morning, of waking up under a heavy pile of bedclothes and realising that none had had the heart to wake me the previous night, I was left to sleep where I lay.

The memories of Britain are made up of intense fragments:*

We are at a banquet, my father is presenting the gifts we brought from home, silks and handicrafts and sacred writings. I can hear the gasps and cries of the women as they unroll the beautiful colours. I can see the tear in the eye of our host as he accepts the Torah my father has brought him.

My father and I are in the damp, early morning garden, walking and talking, our breath sending plumes of mist into the air.

We are at the home of a mine owner carefully examining the quality of the ore that he produces and bargaining over the price.

I am with the daughter of our host, laughing at the way she pronounces certain words while she chides me over my attempts to learn her language. Feeling my youthful stirrings of passion for her gentle ways.

*According to the Master, Josephes travelled to Britain three times during his lifetime, whereas Yeshua never did. David feels that these memories may be from more than one trip.

I am climbing the Tor, reaching the top and almost being blown over by the wind and standing on tiptoe to see if I can catch sight of Jerusalem.

I am sitting on a hillside, enraptured by the long twilight and powerful sunsets of Britain, and all the time, at every encounter, struck by the openness to strangers of the people who live here.

And there are more difficult memories: of cold nights; the tears of homesickness staining my pillow; longing for my mother's understanding and for my family and friends. None of this is discussed with my father, although I think that he guesses. My forbearance earns me his respect, but there are times when I would gladly trade my father's respect for my mother's touch and to feel the strength of the sun warm on my back again.

The harshness of winter gives way to the soft warming of spring, to the blossom in the trees and the bird song in the air. There are no deserts in Britain, every aspect of this land supports growth. With the rising of the sap comes a lifting of my spirits, for my father has said that we will not risk these waters in wintertime again. As the time of our departure comes closer I find myself drawn more and more to the boat and to our preparations for leaving. There are repairs to be made, alterations and carpentry to be undertaken for we learned a great deal from our outward journey. The cabin is strengthened to give more protection from the elements and extra racks are built for jars to hold fresh water. I can hear myself singing as I work.

The day of our departure is here and there have been many tearful farewells. I see the genuine sadness and grief in the eyes of our hosts and the people who have opened their homes to us. I realise how loved we have been during our stay and I feel embarrassed, a little guilty that I cannot offer the same display of emotion in return, but my heart is set on the shores we are headed for rather than the ones we are leaving.

How strange it is that a mile walked on one day can be so much longer or shorter than the same mile walked on the next. It is like this on our way home. It is true that the winds are more favourable on the return journey, and the additional supplies we carry mean that we have to stop less often. But neither of these things can fully explain why time seems to pass so much more quickly for me on our homebound journey. If wanting fills the sails of boats then our sail is made fuller by mine.

I have become something of a symbol of good cheer for our party, for it has become my habit to position myself in the bow of the boat watching intently for the landmarks that we noted on our outward journey. The skipper says that with me at the prow we have no need of any navigational devices, all he need do is follow my nose because he has become convinced that I can smell Jerusalem.

And so it goes, as the days turn to weeks and the weeks to months, the weather with each day becoming warmer, the sun brighter and the light clearer. There are none amongst our party who have not longed for home from time to time, though I believe that as the youngest member I have been afflicted by homesickness more than the others. They may tease my unguarded enthusiasm for our return but I know that in me they see their own yearning for their loved ones, their children and their homes and by encouraging me they keep their spirits up.

As we approach the shores of our country I am more acutely aware than ever before that this is not just my homeland but my heartland. For several days now I have been in a state of calm anticipation. It is hard to describe my feeling, perhaps the closest I can get is to say that it is a kind of very deep knowing, the same as one might feel before meeting an old and unwavering friend. I look out from the boat towards the coastline, at the rugged hills and mountains and the palm trees and vegetation in the foreground. I love this land, with its droughts, deserts and its merciless heat. It is my home, it is where I belong.

It has been over a year. I left as a boy and am returning as a man. I think about my family and especially my mother and Yeshua. I know it is ridiculous but I fear that they may not recognise or remember me. I am anxious that there may not be a place for me.

The simple business of securing our boat in the harbour takes on an added meaning on this day, for I know now that this land is where I truly live, and this land is where I will die. As soon as we are moored one member of the crew sets off to inform the household of our arrival, another makes his way to the port authorities to notify them. In the meanwhile I step on to dry land and quite spontaneously fall to my knees and kiss the ground. I can hear my father laughing approvingly behind me and as I rise I see him following my example beside me. He offers me his arm and together we set off for our home.

All those available to greet us have assembled in the porch and on the stairs. When they see us coming they spill out on to the street to greet us. I cannot see my mother but I know that she will be looking for me. I know that she will want to see my face even before that of her husband. I can see her now standing still and waiting. I approach through the melee surprised that she does not advance towards me. I stop before her. She is looking intently into my eyes, searching for the boy who left her. At first I stand firm, wanting more to present to her my newly won manhood, but I cannot resist her gaze and she finds what she is looking for. She sees the child in my eyes and with it she sees what he has been through. All the things that my stoicism and resolve over the last year have pushed into the background now rush to the surface, and I dissolve into tears and into her arms.

It is a relief to let go to the more sensitive feelings that have been bottled up for so long but it is also deeply confusing. Perhaps it means that I have not progressed as far into manhood as I had thought? As we walk back to the house I imagine that I can feel the eyes of the rest of the party on my back. I begin to feel embarrassed, as if the meeting with my mother is a test that I have failed. I do not let it show and instead of feeling at home I begin to feel terribly alone.

The celebrations begin but I cannot help myself from withdrawing and feeling that I do not fit. I cannot seem to fulfil either the expectations of my mother or my father and I begin to feel a little resentful towards them both. Fortunately my depressing thoughts are interrupted by an arm around my back. I look up and it is Abu, who had stayed behind to watch over the family. He is an extremely sensitive man, tall and broad though not given to speaking much. He is looked up to by both sons of Joseph and when he does have something to say it is usually paid attention to. I am delighted to see him. It would appear that he has observed my dilemma and understood it immediately because he wastes no time in addressing my feelings. 'It is not unmanly to cry, Josephes, it is good. Your tears show your love of your mother, your shame shows your love of your father and your anger demonstrates that you have self-respect. They are all good, none cancels out any other.' His reading of my situation brings an immediate relief, and I look up to see my father observing our discussion from the other side of the room. He sees me looking and after a moment nods slowly and smiles a little smile. I smile back and then turn back to Abu who is asking me about my journey.

The celebration of our return and the sharing of news continues late into the night, and with the encouragement that Abu has given me I am able to join in more fully. Of course my first concern is for the whereabouts of my cousin. It transpires that he is at Qumran and is not expected to return to Jerusalem for several weeks. There is news of him, however, as there are those within the household who visit regularly. I find the man who will be making the journey next; he tells me that Yeshua has been asking after my return. I ask him to deliver a small package on his next trip and this he agrees to do. I pass him the package, a small tightly bound leather wallet, and he promises to deliver it safely into Yeshua's hand.

In the wallet is a small piece of mineral that I brought back from England. I know that Yeshua's studies at Qumran take in a great deal concerning stones. This particular piece was given to me by one of the miners we visited, who claimed that it was most unusual. I make my friend promise that he will guard the package most carefully and that he will give no news of my return to Yeshua until after he has opened it.

It is now over a week since our return and we have been gradually reacquainting ourselves with friends, family and routine. I have hardly seen my father as he has been busy catching up on his lapsed involvements at the Temple. It is a great pleasure to see again the friend who took my package to Qumran. He says nothing, but hands me back the package that I entrusted to him a week ago. My heart sinks as I see it and I ask why he was unable to deliver it. He informs me that he is forbidden to say anything until I have opened it. Immediately I realise what is going on and quickly open the wallet. There inside is a small note; I cannot help but smile as I lift it out. On the note is written the date of Yeshua's return to Jerusalem and beside it is a small piece of mineral, different to the one I sent, with a soft golden colour. I look up at our friend and he asks if it is what I expected. I reply happily that it is, and we walk off together as he tells me the news of Yeshua.

A visit to Lazarus.
We are spending the day visiting the homes of friends. We have both been absent from Jerusalem for an extended period and are both keen to reacquaint ourselves with our friends. We are walking down the hot, sandy-coloured

streets talking and laughing as we go towards the home of Lazarus. He has no idea that we are coming and so when we both arrive he and his sister and mother are beside themselves and make an awful fuss of us. This is received with some glee on our part since we knew that it would be so. If we had conspired to create a better welcome I doubt that it could have been accomplished.

They want to know about Britain and Qumran all at the same time as wanting to tell us all that has transpired whilst we have been away. Yeshua and I engage in the most complicated of discussions as listeners and speakers interject, change subjects, talk over each other and ask questions. It is through discussions such as this, rather than the talks that we have had when alone, that all the details of our lives whilst we have been away are learned. Strangely enough it is not recent history that has been important with those I have met since I returned from Britain but the here and now.

Walking home.
It is a quiet moment. The day that we have just spent with Lazarus and his family has put us both in a reflective mood. Of the two of us I had assumed that in accompanying my father to Britain I had drawn the short straw. Listening to Yeshua today I realise that life for him at Qumran has not exactly been easy either. He is considered outspoken and precocious by many. This has given rise to innumerable and diverse attempts to discipline his thinking and actions. Surprisingly, even at Qumran it would appear that there are precious few who are able to recognise and nurture true talent. The more enlightened may argue that constructive criticism serves to refine a person's position and perhaps they are right, but I can also see how often Yeshua is hurt by the process. Although he can get very angry it is not his way to retaliate or to fight like with like, so not surprisingly the net result of such attention is that he often feels isolated and lonely.

As we walk and talk it seems to me that there may have

been method in the madness of my trip to Britain after all. I find that I have no difficulty in empathising with Yeshua's feelings nor does he with mine. Although the circumstances of my separation from home were different and I was not so burdened by misunderstanding, many of the feelings were the same. Each of us is able to find some solace in the sympathy of the other. It is the first time since my return home that our conversation has taken such a turn and while the topic is painful, it is good to share our deeper feelings and to take heart from the understanding of a friend.

We continue our walk in silence for a while. I can feel the hot, smooth road under my bare feet, cooling with the onset of evening. There is a religious festival tomorrow at which both Yeshua and I are expected. Yeshua wants us to miss it and spend the day together in the hills. I would much rather spend the day with Yeshua but to do so would mean at least an argument with my father or, even worse, disobeying him. It is easier for Yeshua, his parents are used to him disappearing for days at a time. It continues to cause intense worry on their part but they are aware that he does not do it as an act of rebellion, more as a result of his extreme wilfulness. I agree to meet him in the morning; we part company and I set off on the remainder of the walk home, practising my excuses.

It is a delicate business. I start by enlisting the cooperation of my mother, since I know that she will almost certainly agree to my absence. Unfortunately her willingness to accede to my demands in matters such as this sometimes renders her judgment worthy of suspicion in my father's eyes. I ask him nevertheless and am taken almost completely by surprise when he agrees without hesitation. He informs me that he feels that I am old enough to know my own mind in these matters. Although he would wish me to be by his side tomorrow he realises that I have spent a great deal of time in that position recently. He has given a good reply. I feel that he trusts my loyalty and my friendship and in letting me make up my own mind has given me the responsibility for my own decisions. I leave his room with a mixture of feelings: relief, excitement and a little guilt that I will not be with the family on the morrow.

An old friend and a passing.
The air is crisp and the day has hardly started when we meet in the morning. We set off immediately. There is no destination or goal to our day, we do what we have always done: set off and make up our minds on the way. The going is more important than arriving. We are already quite knowledgeable about the area surrounding the city and are well aware of what can be comfortably accomplished in one day's walking. We start towards the hills to the north of Jerusalem and on the way decide to visit an old friend. It is not unusual for us to stop and talk to people on our travels and over time we have met many people of all persuasions, some friendly, some not. The man we are seeking today we met some years previously on a similar day out; he was a poor farmer working his land. We stopped and helped him to gather his harvest and in return he shared his lunch with us. He was quite old then, so we wonder as we walk if he will still be at his farm. When we met him before we were both deeply impressed by his kindness and have often referred to him in conversations since then.

We are passing through the rocky terrain that is where we last met the old man. The land is inhospitable and arid, just sufficient to support the growth of some olive trees. As we approach the old man's property it is clear that all is not as it should be. The olive harvest is over-ripe and much of it remains uncollected. There are signs of dereliction and neglect. We find the exact spot where we shared lunch with him two years ago and sit down. We have brought food and drink with us and as we eat we speculate as to whether the man is still in the vicinity. At the time of our last visit we did not go into his home and so we have no idea where it may be. We decide that after our lunch we will explore the valleys on either side of our position to see if we can find him again.

It is not difficult to find what we take to be his home; it is a poor affair situated in the next valley. We walk down the rough hillside towards it. It consists of one room built of wood, stone and mud, a stable where an ancient donkey is tethered and a store room with a few oil jars stacked outside. Despite the humbleness of the dwelling, the buildings are in good order, the donkey is well cared for and we feel no apprehension in approaching. We are not far from the house when our guess is confirmed and our old friend emerges from the doorway. He stands quite still, stooped and squinting towards us, for it would appear that his eyesight is not good. Even when we draw quite close he has to peer at us quite closely but as soon as he can see clearly he recognises us straight away. He is obviously very distressed and not at all sure whether he should be pleased to see us or not. We enquire after his sadness and he waves towards the door of the house, explaining that his old wife is very sick.

We are a little perplexed, feeling that we have come at an inopportune moment. We start to make excuses to leave but he stops us. He gestures towards the door of the house and begs us to look at his wife. We do as we are bid. The inside of the room is stiflingly hot and the stench of incontinence hits us like a thick curtain. The old man kneels beside the bed and starts to cry, rocking gently to and fro as he does, imploring God not to make her suffer so. We approach the bed and there is the most disturbing sight: the old woman is almost a corpse, emaciated, with sunken eyes, her breath coming in sharp, vicious stabs punctuated by dry coughing. It is my guess that she is in the advanced stages of the coughing sickness. Without hesitation Yeshua kneels at her side and places his hand on her forehead. The transformation is profound: her breathing becomes quiet and the terrible fight that wracks her body begins to subside. A stillness and peace enters her and after one final deep breath she lets go and dies. He looks up at the old man and says, 'She is gone, father.' The old man nods slowly and says, 'Peace be with her.'

The episode is typical demonstration of Yeshua's ability. There are no lightning bolts, no thunderclaps, no hosts of angels or bright lights – at least if there are, they are not visible to the naked eye. Whatever passes between him and those who are in need is entirely natural. Without fuss, without glamour and without drama. Simple and natural. What is unusual about this event is that it is the first time that I have seen him use his power so deliberately, and in the company of someone who is not a close friend or member of the family. It was clear also that the old man recognised him. Not just that he had met him before but that Yeshua had the ability to help his wife's suffering. It would appear to me that even though he sometimes finds life at Qumran difficult there is encouragement enough for him there.

We are outside in the sunshine. The calm that possessed the wife shortly before she passed on has also taken possession of the old man. He takes time to thank Yeshua for his assistance. I stand back a little. The old man's eyes are shining, not with tears but with love. I am deeply touched by what I see before me but I also feel a momentary welling-up of envy. Why should it be him who has the power? Why not both of us, and then we would not be separated in this way? Why not me? They are dark and difficult feelings for an adolescent to have to contain, but my trip to Britain has afforded me ample practice in stoicism.

We leave our friend to bury his wife and start our walk back up the hillside towards the path home. I am still absorbed in wrestling with my demons and so we walk silently. Despite my attempts to be strong it has never been easy for us to keep secrets from one another. I know that I will have to say something. Surprisingly it is Yeshua who speaks first, 'I am sorry, Josephes,' he says quietly. I am confused; it is I who should be apologising not he, and yet there is something in the tone of his voice that indicates that he understands what I am feeling. We walk a little further in silence and after a while he speaks again, 'I feel that I will ask even more of our friendship in time to come.' I know that I will gladly give it.

The pledge!
Wine, dark red wine in a cup. The cup is plain, of dark red clay with a whitish glaze and is spinning slowly. I feel very ill. Yeshua is with me and we have drunk too much. We are no strangers to wine but our imbibing has always been slight, part of family celebrations and supervised by the older members of the family. I have the feeling that my father is away which has encouraged us to make use of the opportunity to experiment. I am promising myself that I will never ever touch drink again.

Physicians all!
I can see an eye, and feel someone's breath on my face. The eye moves back and things fall into perspective. The eye that I could see belongs to my father who was examining my iris. He talks to a man who is standing beside him and they discuss what he has seen. Now the man leans forward and examines my eye. I don't care, I feel so sick. In fact if I were not feeling so ill it would be rather comical having these two take turns to peer into my eyes and then discuss my malady as if I wasn't there. In fact at one point they get quite carried away discussing my illness until I have to interject with a groan to bring their attention back to where I feel it should be. 'Ah yes,' says my father, 'you'll be all right in the morning,' and they exit still discussing the condition of my eyes.

At Qumran.
A plate on a table; there is no food on it. I am sitting at the table with others and we are about to begin a meal. There is fruit and bread on the table as well as olives and water. This is not a formal meal but one where there is talking and laughter. There are family members present as well as others, servants and visitors and the main purpose of the

occasion seems to be to rest and eat. It is the midday meal and I am in a hurry. I have been working all morning and as soon as the meal is over I am going to visit my cousin. As I eat I picture the place he is in. It is neither a school nor temple though it has elements of both: a series of buildings surrounded by a wall which encloses a large green courtyard. It is Qumran and it is where Yeshua is studying. I have been to visit him there before with my father and on occasions, at the direction of my father, I have stayed there for specific studies myself.

I am approaching the building now; the surrounding wall runs alongside a wide dusty road. About halfway along there is an arched entrance with doors that can be closed and this is where Yeshua meets me. He is about thirteen or fourteen years old and we walk together into the courtyard. There are others here of all ages; the younger ones call out or wave when they see me. There is a friendly but studious atmosphere at this place and we walk quite quickly to the side of one of the buildings.

The outer wall and many of the buildings have been built with fairly deep buttresses at regular intervals to support the walls. These have been plastered and whitewashed. We make our way to the cool of one of the alcoves that have been created by this method of construction and sit in the shade to talk privately. We talk of our lessons. Yeshua is learning a great deal here which he shares with enthusiasm. It is clear that he also misses the family and especially his mother, but he explains that there are tutors here who are prepared to challenge the laws and reach a deeper understanding of the truth in doing so. I can see how difficult it is for him; he needs his family but he also needs what this place can provide.

Chapter 4

As a youth

There is a great swirl of dust, the clanking of bells, the braying of a donkey and the dull sound of horses' hooves on the road. I can see a camel's face through the dust. I dislike camels intensely, probably the result of having been caught once as a child by an accurate gob of spit, so I avoid this one. In the middle of the melee I can see a young girl being lifted on to the back of an animal. There are about ten or fifteen people and we are setting off on a journey, the children riding along with the adults. I am on horseback and I ride alongside the party taking care of problems and stragglers and the frequent stops for refreshment. We are returning from the family home in Arimathea to the homes in Jerusalem, a pilgrimage that used to take place two or three times a year before the home in Cyprus was completed for our use.

It has been a long and tiring journey. So much of our lives is taken up with travelling, and it is a dirty and sweaty business. There is no easy way to travel from one place to another in this land; it is time-consuming and hard, so when we finally arrive at the Jerusalem home, stiff and aching, it is with great relief.

In our family life there is no such thing as an empty home. All the houses that are owned and lived in by the Arimatheans are occupied by servants even when there is no family member present. In some ways this relationship between the servants and the household makes our family unique. The Arimatheans are not the only family within the Jewish nobility to treat their servants well but the relationship in our homes goes far beyond that of loyalty to a good master. The servants are accepted as full members of the household, more friends than employees.

The great wheel of history.
I can hear and see sheep below me. It is morning and still

cool although the sun is bright. I can feel Yeshua's left hand on my right shoulder. He is pointing beyond the sheep and explaining something to me. We are still young, not yet fully adult. On the other side of the valley I can see what he is pointing at. There is a small trail that leads up into some rocky hills. We run down the slope scattering the sheep in our path, aware of the shepherds' watchful eye on us. We make our way across the valley, the grass and scrub giving way to a more rocky terrain, and before long what had appeared as small rocks from the other side of the valley loom before us as huge boulders.

We find the trail leading up between two of them and climb up. They are quite a bit taller than us and, immediately we enter, the sun is cut off by their shade leaving the air quite chilly. It is an eerie landscape, a maze of small paths between great rocks, some impassable, some needing a dangerous climb to pass. It is over an hour before we reach the top and select a massive smooth rock on which to climb. It is a good vantage point and we settle down and look back over the way we came.

The air is clear, the sky is the most vibrant azure blue and we have the whole day in front of us. I lie on my back and squint up into the sky, where a few small white clouds are drifting slowly overhead. Yeshua lies down too and we see shapes in the clouds – animals and birds – and we laugh as we see caricatures of some of the people we know. Between the clouds our talk turns to memories of Egypt, of the time we spent there, the friends we made and the many visits with my father to ancient sites. We talk of our visits to the tombs, especially that of Imhotep; it had a profound effect on us both.

We talk of ancient civilisations lost and gone, of teachers and kings, wars and plagues. Although hardly recognised, between the clouds we are glimpsing the great wheel of history slowly turning, all but innocent of the fact that before long virtually all the people we know will be swept up in its great arc.

On becoming a man.
The rustling of silk robes. The robes are on the backs of young priests from the Temple who are hurrying down the corridor in our house. My father has invited them here to stand witness. I am standing in the doorway of a room which leads on to the corridor and I watch their backs as they jostle into the room at the end. They have their own agenda, they are here to learn. Today is an important day for me, too: the young priests are preparing for a ceremony at which, according to our religion, I will be made a man. Behind me and looking over my shoulder is Yeshua. He teases me, 'They are in such a hurry, it must be a very important ceremony that they are going to.'

I don't need telling that. It is all right for Yeshua, he has nearly two years to go before his ceremony. It is a rather complicated affair; there are rules to be observed, words to be spoken at the right time and places where I must stand, sit and recite verse. It is most important to me that I get it right. It is not that there will not be help at hand if I make a mistake – young men are often prompted during the proceedings – but it seems to me that part of being a man is showing an ability to manage without the constant support of parents. There is a deeper fear, too, and it concerns the nature of the vows that I must take. It is not so much that I do not agree with them but I feel that I may fail them, that I am not the right material for them.

It is happening. The room is full of people and they are all very quiet. I can hear my voice speaking as if it is coming from someone else. The rabbi in front of me looks solemn. I can feel my mother's eyes on me. I can feel my father's pride, and I know that my cousin knows just how I feel. It is happening and I am managing very well.

The ceremony is over. I am alone with my father and he is enunciating the list of my responsibilities. Most of them are not a surprise as we have spoken of them many times before, but to hear them spoken in this way, all together, is extraordinary. As the eldest son I will have responsibility for all the family affairs when my father is away. These include all financial matters including overseeing the business interests of our fleet, the mining and timber business as well as the care of all those in the employment of our concerns. In addition to this I have responsibility for overseeing the movements and affairs of all the women members of the household including my sister, my mother and Yeshua's mother; I will be responsible for seeing that all the religious festivals and rites are observed and will be expected to speak at the Temple at certain times of year; and I must commit the religious calendar to memory. I will have to perform all the social functions as head of the family and there are many of these for we are a family of great social standing. To help me in all this there are a list of mentors I must consult if I am in need of advice, including Nicodemus. The responsibility of the elder son is enormous. When the father is away, he becomes the father.

My father speaks firmly and with great emphasis, searching my eyes as he does so to ensure that I have understood what he has said. He is at great pains to point out that our family is a historical one with a great responsibility to the community. The reputation of the house of Arimathea is famous and is held in very high esteem so I must never do anything that will bring the family name into disrepute. On this point he is most pressing. He says that I must behave not just as a Jew but as an Arimathean and not just as an Arimathean but as the heir to the Arimathean household, for when he is away, I am in charge.

I have a mixture of feelings as I hear him talk but mostly I feel numb. All this and I am not yet thirteen years old. It will be many years before I will fully understand the consequences of being given adult responsibilities when virtually still a child. Responsibility and authority grow with life experience and are not inherited. And I have developed a certain amount of arrogance and false confidence to cover my inadequacy, an arrogance that gives me plenty of height from which to fall.

A talisman.

A light sandy-coloured soil that crunches underfoot as we walk. Yeshua is holding something, examining it closely. It is attached to a chain which hangs down from his fingers. It is a pendant with an intricate design of the sun on it, a charm or talisman of some sort. Yeshua manages to open it and takes out a piece of paper with some hieroglyphics on it. He unrolls it and examines it closely: 'It is to ward off evil spirits.' We are both a little disappointed. Such talismans are commonplace and can be bought for a few small coins in the marketplace. Many of them originate in Egypt and the sellers claim all kinds of cures and miracles can be wrought from wearing one around the neck.

Most like us treat such claims with suspicion but some do believe and use them. We believe that there must be a grain of truth in the claims that are made and the faith that some lodge in them and so whenever we come across one we take it to pieces to see if this could be the one that has real power. In fact I don't remember us ever having found one that was of any use other than decoration. Still, it's a nice idea and we both liked the design on this one, brass on a tin ground.

Interpreting the Torah.

The interior of a room. I am looking at a bench set below a window that is too high for me to see out of. The wall behind the bench is old and stained. I look up and to my left; there is a tall man with his arms folded looking down at me waiting for something. I am seated at a desk or table. It is not clear to me whether I am in the room alone with this man. He is my tutor and I am at my studies. On the table before me is a scroll and on it is written a part of the Torah and the tutor is waiting for an answer from me. He has asked my opinion on a point of law. It is a dangerous question since the point he has chosen is a controversial one which is open to several different interpretations and this is the reason that I have paused to reflect before answering. He is aware of my closeness with Yeshua and has made it clear that he does not approve of my association with such a wayward young man. In some ways his question is a test of my cousin's influence.

This tutor has been defeated before in discussions at the Temple by Yeshua's simple logic and he is not above making me pay for his loss of pride. Those verbal skirmishes he loses with Yeshua he delights in winning with me, comparing me unfavourably with my cousin and demonstrating that I have not half his wit. In many ways he is right. While I could answer in the same way that Yeshua would, I have not the same access to the source from which his wisdom springs and so have no way of defending my assertions. I avoid the humiliation of another defeat by giving him the least controversial answer that I can. As he turns away there is a glint of satisfaction in his eye, the brightness of which blinds him to the stone in my heart.

A question of free will.
Palm fronds, forming an arch through which a road passes. The sky is blue, the sun is shining and the air is cool and fresh. In the far distance is the sea. There are fields on either side of the road and in some of them there are people working. Some of them look up to hail and greet us as we pass. We are walking fairly briskly and talking as we walk. It is an earnest discussion, a thorough airing of our views.

There are just the two of us, Yeshua and myself. It is difficult to assess our ages but we are no longer children. The discussion concerns that which we see about us and whether it is right that the land is farmed or whether this is an interference with the will of God as revealed in the natural wilderness. We talk about animals being part of the wilderness since they, like plants, cannot reflect upon their actions. We agree that such philosophical questions can only be asked of man's behaviour since it is only man who is able to ignore his instincts. We discuss whether the instinctual is the repository of natural law and agree that it is but only to a point. Yeshua argues that without free will there would be no opportunity for any being to become aware of their godliness but this capacity also gives man the opportunity to turn against God. The seed in the ground has no choice but that its leaves grow upward and its roots grow downward but man can harvest it, move it, or wilfully destroy it.

It is typical of the discussions we have: not always conclusive but illuminating nonetheless and often quite deep in philosophical content or in attempting to see ourselves as part of a larger picture. We both have good intellects and can debate points quite passionately at times.

Debating with Yeshua.
We are at the Temple again. By now I have accompanied Yeshua on many visits to talk with the scholars and scribes. He always causes a bit of a stir when he arrives. Most of those who are here do not know what to do with him because he does not fit into any of their expectations or categories. Some of the learned men fear him and try to trick him but he always gets the better of them. He can see the traps in their questions and yet he never fights like with like; he simply and authoritatively states the truth, the simple reality.

The mistake that they make is that they always couch their questions and statements in the terms of men who look up to God, feeling themselves to be separate from Him. They try to ingratiate themselves with this God by following laws that they feel will not offend Him. These laws are intricate and detailed and often the scholars' work is more concerned with the interpretation of the words than the spirit that they represent. Yeshua answers simply, not as a man but as one who seems to understand the mind of God intimately, a God who loves all creation and can see the light shining clearly through the maze of words that

His children delight in debating. Yeshua does not patron-
ise or scold like some of the scribes, he simply states what
he knows. In so doing he gently exposes the vanity in the
argument and points the speaker back to the God within.
As a philosopher he is peerless.

There is one amongst the scribes who is particularly
fond of Yeshua. A little younger than the others, he always
welcomes him and those who accompany him. He seldom
joins in the debate though his eyes twinkle at the turns the
discussion takes. Throughout our visit I sit close to him
and also do not join in. Some of the men with whom
Yeshua debates are teachers of mine and they have already
made it clear that they do not care for my close association
with such as Yeshua.

A misunderstanding.
We are walking together in the hills. I am angry and silent.
He is silent as well but I am too engrossed in my own feelings to ascertain what he is feeling. I stamp on ahead,
sensing that he is affected by my feelings and pleased at
this. He is frightened, maybe, or careful; at any rate he
seems at a loss as to how to reach me.

I am angry at something he has done, I want to yell at
him but dare not. I have the impression that he is going
away or doing something without me, and I feel excluded,
as if he does not care about me, but it is more than that, a
premonition perhaps.

I feel his touch on my shoulder, a gentle touch.
'Josephes,' his voice is questioning, appealing, both concerned and loving. I cannot remain angry with him and
give way to the grief; tears come, and through the tears I
hear my voice say, 'Don't leave me.'

We are standing close together. I feel foolish and
relieved, though I cannot look in his eyes. He wipes a tear
from my cheek with his thumb. It is not the first time that
he has done this, or that I have wiped his cheek in the same
manner, and it will not be the last either. 'I won't,' he says
and we walk on slowly, arm in arm.

A discussion with Lazarus.

The market square. Sun-baked, dusty and dry. I am looking down on it from the balcony of our Jerusalem home. I am leaning on the parapet wall. I am a young man. Across the market square comes Lazarus. He is slightly older than Yeshua and myself, tall and a little gaunt with an unmistakable way of walking, as if his body is having to catch up with the direction his head is taking the whole time. He looks up and sees us, grins, waves and quickens his step. We make our way to the back of the house, down the stairs and into the garden where we greet him. It is cool and shaded in the garden since at this time of the day the sun strikes the front of the house.

We sit on the grass and talk. With Lazarus the conversations are always philosophical and spiritual. He has an inquiring mind with a wry and humorous way of looking at things. We continue with an ongoing debate about the Essene tradition. When the sun has softened a little we go down to the market place to buy some small things to eat. There is plenty in the house but we all enjoy strolling around the market and are well known there.

Yeshua's intervention.

A small boat and a group of young men on the shore. There is some bravado or competition in the discussions that are going on. It is known that amongst those present I am the strongest oarsman. Within the group not all are close friends; some are friends of friends and amongst these is one who is the son of a labourer. There is talk of an occasion when I rowed such a boat as the one on the quay to an island in the fastest time of any in our company. I am pleased with the acknowledgement but the labourer's son speaks up and implies in a humorous way that the son of a nobleman has nothing better to do with his time than to practise his rowing. This raises a laugh from everyone including myself but under the laughter I feel the knife of his hostility and am infuriated by it. I turn towards my detractor to engage him but Yeshua catches my eye and holds it. His recognition of what has happened helps me let the issue drop.

Later on when there are fewer present the one who mocked me has occasion to lift something heavy. As he does so Yeshua says softly and to no-one in particular, 'How beautifully he lifts the bag; it must be because he spends his days tilling the soil.' It is said with no trace of malice or sarcasm, simply a statement of fact that all bear witness to. It is a classic Yeshua intervention: the young man does lift the bag beautifully and at a stroke Yeshua affirms the man's beauty, exposes his envy and demonstrates to all the true way.

A visit to an important Roman.
I am sitting on a rock, waiting in the morning sunshine. I am very well dressed, in robes and headgear. The cloth is beautiful, a heavy blue embossed silk from the Orient. The whole ensemble is belted at the waist and upon the belt is a purse and a decorative knife. It is formal dress for a formal occasion.

There are several other members of my immediate family assembled too: my father and sister are there and we are waiting for my mother. They, too, are dressed in beautiful silken robes. We are to be guests in the home of a prominent and wealthy Roman. Such liaisons make our family unpopular with some but my father has always taught that there are the good and the bad among all people, and that integrity is not the property of the oppressed. This does not really concern me however, for whatever the prejudices of parents may be they seldom find lodging in the hearts of their children when they are young. The man we are to visit has a son of my age who I am close to and I am looking forward to spending time with him.

The home of our hosts is a villa of exquisite proportions – it is not all sorrow and oppression that the Romans have brought. It is built on three sides around a garden court-

yard. We are welcomed in a manner that befits our cos-
tumes and it is not long before refreshments have been
taken and my mother and sister are deep in conversation
with the wife of our host. My father and our host are
walking in the courtyard engrossed in some philosophical
discourse and I am free. My friend flicks his head to indicate that I should follow and disappears round the side of
the villa. He is already climbing out of his toga as I
approach and I follow suit and divest myself of my heavy
outer garments. Before I have finished my companion has
climbed the tall wall that flanks the villa and is offering a
hand to me. I clamber up beside him and we sit side by
side on the top. The villa is built on the side of a hill overlooking the city and from our vantage point the whole of
Jerusalem is spread out before us. We sit in silence for a
while, glad to be out of the way of our parents, and listen
to the noise that drifts up the hillside; animals, people's
voices and dogs barking in the distance, and always a pall
of smoke and dust hanging in the air.

We can see the Temple and Golgotha and the house of my
family. He points out the Roman garrison and the school
that he attends, I point out the synagogues, but this is as
far as our differences in background impinge on our talk.
We both share an interest in culture and are widely travelled despite our years and this forms the basis of our discussion, but it is not even this that is important, it is that
friendship dissolves barriers.

A family gathering.
Inside the house the table is being cleared, the cloths that
had covered it are being gathered up by the women. The
table top is laid bare, a polished light oak that bears all the
marks and stains of age, adding to its beauty. I am helping
to carry the table outside into the sunshine, there to be set
and laid for a meal. My father is present, my mother,
brother and sister and friends are here also. We are in a
courtyard of sorts with climbing plants covering one wall,

possibly vine. It is a family mealtime. Pitchers of wine and water are laid on the table with bowls of fruit, plates, jars of oil, salad and clay cups. People are bringing benches and chairs from the house and the women are beginning to sing and dance as they bring the food. There is great happiness and over all this my father presides.

After a blessing the meal begins; I am seated next to my mother. There are about three independent conversations going on all at the same time. It is such a pleasure to have the company of friends and family. It is not that our family is particularly different from any other in this respect. All the Jewish families are large and all have strong bonds of loyalty. There are tensions, jealousies, rivalries and differences, of course, but within our family there is also a deep sense of purpose, unrecognised by many but there nonetheless.

I watch my father across the table. He is neither harsh nor oppressive; quite the opposite. He is strong willed and can be forceful but he is no oppressor, he is the patriarch. He provides not just resources but an atmosphere wherein each one has a place and in knowing that they have a place they are able to be fully themselves. This is partly because in our society it is the patriarch who takes responsibility for the misdemeanours of the family. It creates a family environment wherein which he is responsible to each and each is responsible to him. It is not a question of two being the same or one being better or worse than another because the foundation stone of the family is diversity, a diversity that is possible because of the degree of belonging that each one feels, and my father represents that which we belong to: our faith and the house of Arimathea.

The meal is over, the wine is drunk and it is night-time. The courtyard is lit by little clay oil lanterns. We are sitting loosely round the tables or leaning back in our chairs watching two of the women singing and dancing together. It is a spontaneous event, not uncommon at family gatherings. My father loves these times and although he is quietly effusive in encouraging the dancers his words are not needed, the obvious joy and pleasure he derives from watching would be encouragement enough to move the whole Roman army to dance.

There is laughter and joking as the women flirt with the men, then the men are encouraged to join them in the dance. There is a great deal of humour and delight in those who watch that is evident in the way they applaud and clap in time with the singing. Finally my father himself rises to perform a graceful and stately dance with my mother which is greeted by much love and approval.

A family scene.
A roll of cloth, of pale blue cotton. There is some barter going on, some business being done. I am in a market-place, not too full. It is morning, the sun is bright but the air is not yet hot. The cloth is of good quality, firm and cool under my hand. I am responsible for buying it. A deal is struck and I carry the cloth home on my shoulder. I show the cloth to my mother who is pleased with the quality and the price and will have the cloth made into undergarments for the family. She fits the cloth around me to ascertain the correct length.

Yeshua is sitting in a chair close by, watching and talking; he is waiting until my mother is finished so we can go out. It is a quiet and domestic family scene. My sister comes in but my brother seems not to be in the house. Father is away, too, possibly abroad. My sister is confident and single-minded. She talks with Yeshua who is fond of her. The house is cool, it has thick stone walls. I become impatient to be outside in the sunshine. My mother finishes and we leave.

A birth.
Sun, hot sun, and the smell of animals: sweat, urine and dung. We are in a market, an animal market, where there are donkeys and goats and some sheep. I make my way towards Yeshua who is beckoning and excitedly pointing

into a pen. In the pen is a donkey giving birth to a foal. Squatting beside them is an old man wearing a dirty turban, who tends the mother carefully until the foal is fully out. He beams up at us with a broad toothless grin on his brown face, very happy and obviously deeply moved for there is a tear in his eye. We grin back, both very struck by the beauty and innocence of the foal but also by the attitude and humility of the old man.

As we walk away Yeshua says that creation needs no help nor interference from man, only to wonder at it as we had seen the old man do. He says that the old man had the right attitude towards the birth of the foal: to be moved to tears by it. He says that this is all that the Creator requires of man: to witness creation and be moved to tears by it.

The shadow of the cross.

He rises from the bowl, hands covering his face, water dripping down. He is tired, finding it hard to stay awake. He has been up all night alone. He seems troubled, finding something very hard to accept. He shakes his head disbelievingly, he has no words to articulate his feelings. I feel helpless to comfort him. He looks out of the window as if seeking some escape. Finally the tears come. His pain is so deep that I cannot but cry with him.

In time he talks, quietly, of premonition, of pressure, of things too vast to understand. He cannot make sense of what is being asked of him or why. He talks of his foreboding, of his fear for the future. He turns to me, seeking a glimmer of reassurance in my eyes but I have none to offer, I am as uncomprehending as he. At least there is some comfort in this. He takes my forearm in his hand, 'You are a good friend, Josephes.' We walk slowly back to the house, each deep in thought.

The beauty of nature.

Distant hills and a cold wind on my face; it is evening and a storm is brewing, the clouds dark and ominous. The storm breaks and we run to the shelter of a rocky outcrop.

It is dry underneath. The rain is hard and the thunder cracks. We push our backs into the shallow shelter to avoid the stinging rain and become absorbed by the stupendous power of the elements.

The storm is as short as it is powerful. As it moves on, the air smells fresh and clean and the sound of water trickling down the rocks is in stark contrast to the thunder. Yeshua reaches down into the wet soil and lifts a handful between us. There is nothing dispassionate about nature, he says, what is given is given completely, given with passion and received with a hunger. It is a passion that transforms what was barren into that which is fertile. It is not just something that happens but an urgent love affair.

Josephes observes the Sanhedrin at work.
I watch as two wealthy old men enter a room. I am standing outside and to their right with my father. One of the men is wearing a particularly beautiful silk robe interwoven with gold threads. When they have entered, others follow, each dressed in accordance with their rank, wealth and position in society. As my father enters I fall in by his side. There are several such as I, the sons of various council members who are being tutored in the affairs of their fathers; it is quite normal.

From these meetings and from the discussions with my father that ensue I am able to gain great insight into the workings of the Sanhedrin and the politics of our country. There is an uneasy bond between the occupying forces of Rome and the Jewish authorities. There is a spectrum of opinion on both sides as to how this relationship should best be conducted. There are those on the council who bow their heads to Rome and feel that the interests of the Jews are best served by keeping quiet. They justify their position by arguing that it is the Temple and the spiritual identity of the Jews that must be preserved even if it means sacrifices at another level. My father disagrees with this view; he believes that the spiritual practices of the Jews mean nothing if they are not lived. In this context he is a radical and is often berated for expressing more humanitarian views than those who currently hold the power in the council.

Much of the debating that is witnessed by the young wards of the council members is debated fiercely again within their own company. More often than not the views that are expressed are not dissimilar to those of their fathers. I tend to be even more radical than my father and this, too, is not uncommon. Conservative and liberal alike tend to extend the propositions that they hear their fathers take up and this leads to quite heated exchanges at times.

Debating hypothetical situations.
We are quite high up. I am looking towards the skyline, where the hills and mountains meet the sky in a blue-grey mist. All around me is the rugged pale terrain of the outskirts of Jerusalem. The sun is hot, it is approaching midday and it is time that we found somewhere to rest in the shade. We climb the side of a hill off the main path and sit in the shade of a rocky outcrop taking advantage of what breeze there is. I sit with my knees up and my back against the rock and Yeshua lays alongside, his head propped on his elbow. From our vantage point we can see for miles over the arid deserted landscape, the rocks shimmering in the hot dry air.

Much of our discussion on these trips is about the small things that interest and concern us and much is in the realm of the imagination. We create new and strange scenarios and ask each other what we would do if this thing or that befell us.

He asks me what I would do if my father died. We are both aware of his own father's advanced years and I know that he sometimes wishes that he had a father like my own, young and strong, who takes an active role in the lives of his children. It is a strange irony that I sometimes envy the freedom that his father's advanced years afford him. Of course to my own father Yeshua is like a son but it is not the same. Our situations are different, as well. Yeshua has older stepbrothers who care for the family affairs and this, too, gives him a certain freedom, whereas I am the eldest son and this carries a different responsibility.

'I suppose that I should have to take on the business and run the family as best I could.' I reply. He thinks for a moment then asks, 'And what if you did not want to, what if your destiny lay elsewhere?' Now it is my turn to think. 'My father has a family and yet follows his path, why should not I?'

Yeshua counters my question with yet another: 'But his path and his family are not so far apart. Suppose that it could not be so?' 'Heaven forbid that I should be faced with such a situation,' I reply, 'but I think I would try to do what my father would wish.' He thinks for a long moment and replies, 'I think I would, too.'

At the house of Lazarus.
We are sitting at the side of a well, on a small parapet wall. We are in a small village. Each of us is washing his feet, taking water in a small receptacle that is provided for this purpose. The water is cool and clear and feels good on my feet. We have walked some distance to reach this place and are hot and tired from the sun and the road. There comes a young woman, Mary the sister of Lazarus, and she kneels to assist us. She is perhaps fifteen years old and we are a little older. There is great affection between us and particularly between her and Yeshua. We sit and talk of the journey, of news of recent events and then make our way to her home.

It is cool inside and I have the impression that this is a scholarly home; there are scrolls and writing materials and there is an atmosphere of study and of learning. Lazarus welcomes us effusively and shows us a scroll. He unrolls it on the table and we discuss what is written there. The content is religious in nature and tells of the teachings of the Egyptian schools. We find parallels with the Judaic and Essene traditions and this convergence forms the basis of a lively discussion. There is an element of excitement in the discovery of the spiritual links and laughter at the humour of Lazarus who has a bright mind and a quick wit.

Again the shadow of the cross.
We are standing on a high balcony, leaning on the parapet wall looking down at the people below. We could be at the Temple or perhaps some public building. People are going about their business, leading animals, talking, visiting a couple of stalls selling things. Nobody looks up.

Yeshua says that our present perspective is like that of the Creator. He is always looking down on creation aware of all that passes, and yet those within his creation are so intent upon the detail of life they seldom look up and acknowledge their origins. He says that it will take something truly significant for them to remember.

There is a gravity in his voice and a sadness. He has confided in me several times the premonition that his life may be sacrificed to this purpose. I know the truth in what he says. Our eyes meet briefly and the sadness and burden is acknowledged; there is a tacit agreement between us that this must be. We make our way along the balcony and into the crowds below.

An intimate family moment.
A table, a large wooden table made of thick boards, worn smooth with use. There is a smell of aromatic oil. On the table are some objects, an amethyst stone, a bottle, perhaps containing the oil, some robes, a book and a clay lamp which provides the only light in the room. Joseph, my father, is standing behind the table reading from his scrolls. I can see a gold ring on his finger, I think the stone is purple. I can see his blue eyes in the lamplight against his dark skin and hear his silk robe as he moves. He has great presence and depth. He finishes reading, sits and looks up, his gaze steady. I am perhaps eighteen or nineteen years old and we are in his study.

We talk, of business and of the family. His duties at the Temple take up much of his time and he is beginning to rely on me to handle the estate and some of his other business interests. I feel good about this, more responsible and more equal. He asks about my mother, knowing that sometimes she confides in me more than in him. I feel his concern and talk of her and of my brother and sister, he speaking of his feelings and I of mine. I feel the love between us; it is seldom spoken but on this occasion the natural tension between father and son is absent. I see the man and also feel that he is appreciative of the man in me. There is a tacit acknowledgement of this meeting although it is difficult for us to share our deeper feelings with one another. At the end of our talk he reaches over and covers my hand with his and our eyes meet. It is a moment of tenderness and of understanding.

A simple teaching.
I can feel a gentle cool breeze. I am sitting on a grassy bank overlooking the sea and I can feel the dry grass sharp under my hands. I am with Yeshua and we are talking, leaning back on our arms. There have been many hours spent like this, sharing ideas, thoughts and hopes. On this occasion the talk is political in nature: of the Pharisees and of the religious persuasions of the many opposing groups who populate the area.

Yeshua talks of water, of how every person must drink and how none can survive without a supply of clean water, no matter what their race or habits may be. Water, he says is like the love of the Father: all drink it and all are united in their need of its life-sustaining properties, the only true difference between people is in how it is drunk – from cupped hands, a goblet or a mountain stream – but the water is common to all. If those in religious opposition to one another would realise this, it would be the water that would be important, not the vessel from which it is drunk.

The buying of silver.
A wooden bucket being lowered into a well. It is pulled up and the water is emptied into a crude trough alongside for

the animals to drink. It takes several buckets to fill the trough and only when the horses are drinking do I and my companions quench our thirst. I am travelling with my father to another part of the country on business. So much of our time is spent away from home these days, either alone or together. On this occasion we are travelling together because we are to purchase silver which we will carry back personally. The safety of trips such as this is of paramount importance and is primarily assured by the strict secrecy that surrounds the dealing in precious metals. This trade is therefore restricted to a small circle of honourable men who can be trusted to keep their council. Despite this there is always the risk of an unprovoked or chance attack and this is why we are several banded together. When we have taken our refreshment we climb stiffly back on to our horses and continue our journey.

My father has his servant for company; they are very close and on those occasions when they travel together they form a strong though quiet bond. They do not mean to exclude me, it is just that the paths are narrow and they enjoy one another's company. When they can they ride along side by side, with me behind trying to catch the drift of whatever conversation they may engage in.

From my position behind my father and Abu it is hardly necessary to ride, my horse simply follows theirs as horses do. The drone of their voices, the heat of the sun and the rhythm of the hooves puts me into a drowsy daydreaming state. I am thinking of a young Arab girl that I have taken a shine to. It is not permitted that such liaisons take place but they do. She likes me very much and in truth I would far rather not be on this trip, having to content myself with delicious fantasies. I would rather be back at home in her delicious company.

A humiliating love affair.
I can feel a hand at my back and I am pushed with unnec-

essary force through a door. It is a dark room, stone walls. Before I have a chance to turn round the door is closed and locked behind me and I am suddenly alone. Along one wall is a straw mat that serves as a bed. High on the wall beside it there is a small window. It is just beyond the reach of my fingertips, more of a missing stone than a window, and it is the only source of air and light in the room. It is impossible to see out of it; all that it will tell me is whether it is night or day. I stand staring for some time at it until the thought occurs to me that I am probably in shock. I look down at the bed; I want to sit on it but irrationally feel that if I do, it will mean that I have accepted being here. Without warning I vomit.

I am awakened by the stench. The heat and smell are unbearable. I have had no visitors since I was cast into this cell and there is no water. If I were not so dehydrated I feel sure that I would be sick again. It is daylight at least, I can tell by the light filtering in through the little hole high on the wall. I turn up my bed and stand on it to try to get my face closer to the air; it helps a little. I still cannot believe that I am here. I was taken from the street without warning and I do not even know if my family have been informed of my plight.

My thoughts are interrupted by the door of the cell being unlocked and thrown open. The light streams in and I blink at the silhouettes of two legionnaires who are cursing me and arguing about who should go in to the stench to get me. I save them the trouble and step outside. They march me quickly through the garrison and I am brought before an officer, a fairly low-ranking one, who addresses me in Greek. It occurs to me that his ability to speak Greek is probably why he has been chosen for this task. His scholarliness however has not affected his capacity for officiousness or contempt. It is clear from the way he speaks to me that he hates his position, hates this country and hates Jews. He informs me that I am charged with failing to keep my desires within my own community. He states the evidence against me, some of which is correct and some of which is not, and then asks me if I have anything to say.

I am dumbfounded, partly because the 'offences' he has described are so petty and partly because the only way that he could have obtained some of the knowledge that he has is through my trust having been betrayed by someone close. As I am thinking I can hear him speaking again, about the dangers of mixing blood and of how the Jews must keep their place. I say nothing. He waits for a moment and then talks to the guards in their own language. I understand the Roman slang for Jew in his words, and then he turns to me and with exaggerated politeness suggests that I may like time to consider my position. With a nod to the guards I am dismissed and ungraciously dragged back to my cell.

I am back in the stink and things are beginning to fit together. I feel anger, despair and utter rage at the man who put me here. I am here because of my love of his daughter. We are of the wrong faiths to be seeing one another and he has got the Romans to do his dirty work for him. When I get out, I will kill him.

I am being marched toward the stables. It is only now that I realise the fate that awaits me, for it is in the stable yard that beatings are administered. It is hard to describe my feelings as I am brought into the covered yard. By the time we reach the entrance I have resolved that, whatever may befall me, my captors will not have the pleasure of seeing the effects of their work on my face. The stable yard has two men in it, a commander and one other. I ask the commander why I have been brought here but he ignores my question and indicates to the legionnaires to prepare me. My back is bared and I am forced to kneel before a low wall, against which the two men pin my arms. Not a word is uttered, no pronouncement has been made, no judgment given and I do not know how many times the lash is to descend on my back. After the first cut the pain becomes excruciating. Each stroke takes my breath away, and it is almost impossible to hold on to my determination to remain silent, but I do. It is the fury I feel towards the father of my friend that helps me defy the pain.

Ten lashes.

Bastards.

I am permitted no self-respect in this punishment. As soon as the beating is over I am hauled to my feet rather than being allowed to stand, and not a word has been spoken. The commander dismisses me with a flick of his head. I am not sure what to make of the look in his eyes as they catch mine; there is no emotion there, this is a job to him and he shows no more regard for me than a stock man would to a goat. It is typical of the Romans: their administration shows no regard for the dignity or position in society of those they deal with; we are all foreigners to them and punishment is swift, brutal and summary.

I am half-marched, half-dragged through the yard and the corridors to the main gate and thrown unceremoniously through it. I stumble out into the strong light of the street and start to fall but catch myself, embarrassed by my half-naked state. I hurry to pull my clothing up around my shoulders and move unsteadily away from the door. I am aware of people staring and of others making sure that they do not, but my eyes are fixed to the ground. I just want to get away; if I look anybody in the eye I know I will be unable to hold my feelings at bay.

It is only when I reach the safety of the narrow alleyways on the other side of the street that my legs start to give way. I turn abruptly and sit on a low wall with my back to a building. I can feel a darkness and despair begin to well up inside me but I fight it back. It is strange how strength can be gained from the denial of feelings, but it is strength and numbness that I need at this time. When I have collected myself I continue on towards the home of Yeshua, which is nearer than mine, but I cannot avoid some of the feelings, and the worst is that of degradation and humiliation. I do not feel defiant or even rebellious, I feel wretched.

It is a merciful sight that greets me when I finally arrive at the house of Yeshua for both his mother and my own are present. They look up, quite startled by my appearance and I can contain myself no longer. My mother is seated and I throw myself at her feet. I can hear her asking over and over what has happened but I am in no position to answer for I am possessed of a bitterness and darkness that renders me speechless. And then the unfairness of what has befallen me loosens my tears and I am racked with sobs; they would not have done this if my father had been in the city. As my sobbing subsides I can feel the tender hands of Mary on my back, as she sponges warm water on to my robe to soften the blood that has dried and stuck the garment to my skin. I listen to the soothing voice of my mother as she gently rocks my head in her lap.

The irony of my position does not escape me for I am kneeling in much the same position as I was made to kneel for the beating I received, but now it is love not hatred and indifference that is being administered. It is the same posture of supplication but the attitude of those I am subject to is as different as it possibly can be. Love given freely, no judgment. I know that this is a gift beyond price but I cannot accept it. I am still in prison, only now the walls that surround me are made not of stone and iron but of shame.

I am lying face down on a couch in my own home. It is afternoon, time is slow and I am thinking about the events of the last few days. I feel that I understand now what lesson I was supposed to have learned from this flogging: a respect for the rules, a respect for the Empire. In fact I have learned the opposite, for with each stroke of the lash what little respect there was in me evaporated until now there is absolutely none left. It is not the Romans I despise, there are both the gentle and the brutal amongst them; I despise imperialism itself and the lizards who suck up to it. It is a harsh reminder that these people do not occupy our country because they have been invited, or because they have won the hearts of the people. Their administration is based on fear, intimidation, bullying and greed, and I am damned if I will show respect to such things.

There is one benefit that has come of my experience and it is that I now know for sure. I had not realised prior to this event the degree to which my thinking had been affected by being raised in a country occupied by a foreign army. Somewhere the message filtered through to me that as Jews we were unable to manage ourselves or our country, that we were inferior. But now I know for sure that the Romans are not superior to us, for any administration that can flog a man for following his heart cannot be superior. Now I know for sure, it is not me who should hang his head in shame. By their actions they have demonstrated that it is they who are afraid, afraid of freedom, of human dignity and self-determination. It is a strange knowledge to have, akin to a kind of intimacy. Now that I have experienced their barbarism at first hand I feel that I no longer have any reason to fear them, and yet in another way I fear them even more.

There is some comfort in this. To shift the anger from myself on to the Empire, and then to see myself as a victim of Roman oppression moves the emphasis from my personal transgressions to a place where I can feel almost justified in my actions, but unfortunately it does not last long.

Someone is holding up a robe for me and I step into it. It is heavy, made of closely woven cotton, fresh, white and clean. It is several days now since my encounter with the guard and I have been soaking in a bath of healing salts for my back. The healing is progressing well for the cuts were more livid than deep. The truth is that I could have gone out even two days ago but I have been avoiding it. I had not even admitted it to myself until this moment but am afraid that everyone will know of my degradation. I know that I will have to face my friends and acquaintances before long but I cannot find any equilibrium in myself and if I can put it off another day then I will.

It is a difficult time: by day I fight to restore my pride but by night my efforts are betrayed. I am awake now, in the smallest hours, and I cannot stop my mind going over and over the events of the last week. I am reduced now, my heart eaten away by the hungry worm of self-doubt.

There is an awful fear that I carry deep inside, a fear that moonlight illuminates in a way that sunlight does not. I fear that I am in truth a liar, nothing more than an empty shell with no real substance or depth, lacking the talent of my cousin and lacking the power of my father. If I could step back I would see that it is not surprising that I feel this way, being so close to both, but rationality has no part in the proceedings tonight. Like a scorpion driven to self-destruction, I mercilessly seek out and sting each one of my insufficiencies.

The self-loathing that springs from feelings of inadequacy is bitter indeed. If I were to catch a man treating an animal as I treat myself on these occasions I would strike him down. I know that what I feel is generated from within, it is mine to overcome. I also know that such feelings yield to compassion alone, but until I can forgive myself for being who I am, or until sleep relieves me this night, I must suffer the burden of self-hatred.

Over the days and weeks that follow nothing is truly resolved. I function, I go out, life uneasily returns to normal and I try to put my problems behind me, but in truth the war in my heart continues. On the one hand I will not accept that I have done anything wrong at all and on the other hand I secretly feel that I am a contemptible fool; the feelings are utterly irreconcilable. I start to look to my father's return for hope. I feel that when he comes back he will be able to make sense of it all, he will understand. I imagine myself explaining the circumstances to him and how he will take my side against the cruel injustice that has befallen me, he will put the father of the girl in his place and will use his influence amongst the Romans to obtain an apology.

When he does return it is too late for me to explain anything. I can see him now standing framed in the door, his hands on his hips and his eyes blazing with anger. I start to speak but the words die in my throat. For a moment I think he is going to attack me physically but instead he strides up and down the room bellowing with rage.

He is absolutely beside himself: I have behaved badly, I have brought shame and disgrace on the house of Arimathea, I have no discipline, I am incapable of curbing my desires and above all I am selfish and arrogant. I stand pale and in shock. Finally he stops his tirade and stands glowering at me. I turn and run from the room. I barge past my mother in the corridor without catching her eye and out into the garden.

Now my misery is complete; there is nowhere left to turn. I just walk. Never before in my entire life have I felt so alone, so bereft and so without hope.

It is the desert that calls me, it reflects my mood: barren with no place to escape. I sit with my back against a rock. This is the place that I have been avoiding for the last three weeks. Now that there is no-one to blame for my actions and no-one to rescue me from the consequences, I have no option left but to turn to myself. I knew what I was doing, I knew the penalties. It is irrelevant whether the penalties were just or not, the fact of the matter is that I tried to avoid them by assuming I could use my position and the name of our house and family, and that was arrogant. I can see now that in this respect my father was absolutely right.

I feel my pride soften and a gentleness and understanding well up from within me. For the first time in this episode I am able to let my tears flow for myself. I am only eighteen years old and I have a great responsibility to carry, it is not surprising that I will make mistakes in learning how to handle it. I have done nothing bad. Foolish perhaps, irresponsible, disrespectful of the law, but my actions were motivated initially by affection not hatred. I am not a bad person and if they cannot recognise it, then it cannot be helped. What is important is that I recognise it myself, and with this recognition I gain back some of my dignity and self-respect.

I do not know how long I have spent in the desert; at some point I must have fallen asleep for it is now dawn. I get up and make my way directly to the home of the girl. It is a modest house, with a garden and ornamental vine in front of it. There is no sight of her; I imagine that she has been punished as severely as I have. Her father hears me coming and steps into the garden, barring my way to the house. He is aggressive, wanting to know why I have not learned my lesson yet. I state simply that I have come to apologise, and then do so. He cannot resist rubbing my face in it, though, and implies that I have been made to come by my father. I think that perhaps I asked for this, too. I feel his contempt, but it is no different from the contempt that I showed him when I continued to see his daughter against his wishes. I reply that I came of my own volition and somewhat clumsily bid him goodbye. He calls after me saying I should never come back. I walk on praying that I can contain my desire to retaliate verbally. I did not apologise for my father, neither did I apologise for him, or for his daughter. I apologised for myself.

I start my walk home, aware that the difficulty of what I have just accomplished is nothing compared to the task that lies before me. I make my way into the house, hoping that I will meet my mother and be able to gauge his mood from her. I have no such luck though. I go to the door of his room and hear his voice, calm and familiar bidding me enter. He does not know who it is yet. I venture in and he looks up. I am wary but I know that my eyes are clear and I hold his gaze. I can read nothing in his look so I speak my apology: it comes out stilted, formal, but it is said with true humility. He nods and says, 'Very well, Josephes,' and I leave the room. I know that he has not finished with me yet and I feel a little disappointed that he is maintaining his austere attitude to me. I will have to earn his respect again and he can be a hard master.

It will be many years before I fully understand why his rage on that day was so fierce, and why he found it so hard to forgive me, many years before the truth of his own indiscretion surfaces. For he, too, had transgressed the boundaries of our faith, and had a child by another woman, a sister, raised separately and kept secret from us all, known as Mary Magdalene.

It will be many years before I realise that when he raged at me on that day, he was raging at himself as well.

Yeshua foresees his death and shares the knowledge with Josephes.
A dead tree in a barren, rock-strewn landscape. All the bark and the finer branches of the tree have long since been eroded by the elements, leaving it silvery and stark in the early dawn light. It is hard to imagine now how the tree ever grew at all, the land is so unsupportive, but whatever water once nourished it has been gone for years. I lean on a low branch and press my cheek against the trunk, the wood is soft and smooth against my face. I quietly settle down to wait.

The sun is well up when in the distance I see a figure approaching through the heat haze. He appears to be riding on a donkey. As he draws closer I realise that he is not riding the donkey but leading it. It must be Yeshua, only Yeshua would give his feet to save his companion's hooves. When he is within talking distance he hails me and explains that he had to bring her, they would not let him leave without her to ride on. I give him a look and he says rather apologetically that he may ride her back. He lets her tethers drop and we embrace. We have the whole day to spend together.

Life at Qumran has changed him. He is not an ascetic as such, nor is he against pleasure; quite the contrary, he loves life and lives it to the full. It is just that he has developed his own ways of doing things. I have heard that he perplexes his teachers as much as everyone else, like leading the beast that was given for him to ride, and then treating it as an honoured companion. He has a way of not going against but going with. That with which he comes into contact he touches gently and leaves unscathed.

It is difficult to say whether it is the influence of Qumran that has wrought these changes or whether they come from a deeper source. I think that he uses the teachings to define his own understanding rather than to learn from directly. I understand something of the regime, having been educated for short periods there myself. But it did not suit me. I found the discipline too dry and preferred the society of my own family and all that it offered.

It is the first time that we have had a chance to meet since the humiliation of my beating, which is already now some months in the past. During the intervening time I have been working assiduously to earn back my father's respect. In fact this is the first prolonged stay I have had away from the home and the business since that time. I know that Yeshua has already heard about it, though; such news travels fast, even to Qumran.

It is the immediate topic of conversation, not from my side but from his. He wants to know all about it, every detail: my father's anger and the anger of the father of the girl, he wants to know how I felt when her father yelled at me after I apologised and how the lash felt, and the attitude of the Romans; he wants to know in turn how each member of the family reacted and for how long; whether I still have the marks on my back and whether my father has relented. It is easy for me to tell. Although he spares my pride by not asking the obvious about whether I have learned anything, I am able to supply the answers to even these unspoken questions. In the last months I have faced up to many unpleasant truths about myself and feel that I am richer, wiser and more gentle for it. The discussion takes quite a long time. He is sympathetic and listens carefully and with gravity as I talk, occasionally interjecting for more clarity or to laugh at my dark jokes about the affair.

When finally my story is exhausted he pauses for a moment and then pronounces that my adventure was real living. He is genuinely full of admiration, and even a little jealous I suspect. That my troubles should have such an impact on him I find quite an irony. I brought my suffering on myself through arrogance and a lack of consideration for others. In a way I deserved what was coming to me and yet this man, who is celibate, who walks barefoot through the desert, who spares the back of a donkey, no doubt causing himself considerable pain and discomfort in the process, who chooses difficulty rather than trying to avoid it and then being trapped by it against his will, has no reason to be impressed by my ordeals.

I put this to him by repeating what he has said: 'So you find my suffering to be worthy of your admiration, cousin?' He nods emphatically. I gesture with my chin towards his feet which are bruised and bloody from the long walk here. 'Then tell me of this.'

There is a long silence before he answers. Finally he says, 'When you went through your ordeal your eyes were opened, were they not?' He pauses and I respond affirmatively. 'Well, my eyes have been opened, too, and what I have seen...' his voice trails off. Whatever it is that he has seen is clearly not readily rendered into words. 'I do not have your advantage, you see...' Another pause, and then he says quietly, 'For you illumination is a backward look. You do not know what will happen to you until it does, and only when it has can you see the sense of it. It is my burden to have seen the future. I have seen what is to befall me and I must prepare myself. I must walk on these two feet to the end, and Josephes, my life will end before yours, it will end when our own people turn against me and all that I stand for.'

I am stunned. There is something about his words, spoken without drama and with absolute acceptance and conviction, that prevents me from arguing or questioning. We sit contemplating what has been said. I think that he is as shocked by what he has said as I am. There is nothing really to say; we each look at the ground, avoiding each other's eyes.

I do not think that I can fully comprehend the implications of our discussion. Perhaps the spiritual part of Yeshua can carry the burden of knowing exactly when and in what manner he will die, but what man can carry such a weight? The absurd thought crosses my mind that he is not strong enough, he is just too thin. Then I begin to understand why it is that he walks barefoot. Bruised feet cannot flee.

Josephes in trouble with the Sanhedrin.
A table. Around it are standing four or five older men, including my father who has his fingertips on the wooden surface. All are dressed in their robes of office for they are all members of the Sanhedrin. I am dressed in my best clothes, too. After prayers have been said the men sit down. I remain standing as a mark of respect. Once the men have made themselves comfortable I am invited to sit at the head of the table, with my father to my right. This gathering is a kind of court. All the men are scholars and all are well versed in matters of Jewish law.

The eldest of the priests addresses me. He explains that

they have gathered here to hear me account for my actions in respect of the young girl. He is neither persecuting nor over-friendly, concerned more, I suspect, about the law he represents than about me. He goes on to say that they must decide whether my actions were those natural to a young man, the madness of youth he calls it, or whether they were malicious. If it is decided that my behaviour was to do with youthful indiscretion then they will understand.

After all, he says, many of them have sons of my age and they were all once the sons of fathers themselves. He continues to say that they realise that young men do not find their way in the world through the example and advice of their fathers alone but they must learn from their own experience. If this is the case, he says that my actions will be rewarded by nothing other than their normal consequences and whatever I may learn from them.

Although no tension is betrayed in his voice, I know that my presence here has created some. In the eyes of some of these men it is not just me whose actions are being questioned but those of my father, too. They disapprove of his liberal attitudes toward his children.

The Elder goes on: if it is found that my actions were malicious, then this would not be tolerated, especially by the son of one of their number, a young man given every opportunity in life, the holder of an important position in society and one who is expected to set an example to the other young men of the city.

The old fools, you would think that they had never felt their loins stir. I know their sons, they did not enter the world through chastity. I also know what some of their sons get up to and I cannot bear their fathers' hypocrisy. But I love my father and I know that my behaviour and acceptance by these men is very important to him. We have spoken about this day for some time. We have already made our peace, and he has said that I must use this opportunity to account to God for my actions and not to his representatives. When I think of this my attitude softens and I am able to listen to the man who is speaking. As my anger subsides I begin to feel the humiliation of having to be here in this way. I have already received a beating from the Romans for my troubles and now I have to bear the intimate details of my affections being discussed. It is ridiculous to expect passion to respect the boundaries of religions. One may as well expect a horse not to wander.

To their great displeasure I say as much. A bad mistake. Eighteen-year-olds do not talk back to the Sanhedrin. Particularly eighteen-year-olds who are not as articulate as them, who cannot put their arguments as succinctly, who do not have anything like their life experience and who address them as if they are equals. If I learn anything from the ensuing argument it is that what is permissible within our family and what is permissible in our society are two totally different things. On our journey home, when my father's blood has cooled sufficiently, he points this out to me in fairly colourful terms. Had it not been for his presence, he says, I would have undoubtedly earned myself another scourging. It is difficult to accept these words from the man I admire so much. In truth I want to impress him, but I always seem to end up depressing him.

The son is father to the man.
I am at the family home in Arimathea looking at a red clay urn, quite large, over knee height. It is Roman in design and is standing on a paved area set against a yellowish wall. The urn is filled with clean clear water and stands to the right of a doorway. The door is wooden, oak I think, with a slatted grille. It is open, dark inside and I can see the outline of a window set in the wall on the other side of the room as I look inside.

I enter the room; it has a cool flagstone floor with some rugs over parts of it and some pieces of furniture scattered about. In one of the chairs is seated an old man; he beckons me over and I sit opposite him. He is grey-haired and bearded and although very wealthy lives without ostentation in this section of the main house. He is very old, quite frail and I have mixed feelings toward him: he is the patriarch, the senior father within our large family and although I know he loves me deeply I also have some fear of his position. His eyesight is poor and he beckons me closer to look at my face. He takes my face in his hands and I can feel them tremble, warm and very soft, as he turns my face to catch the light. He smells of cedar wood. 'You have your mother's looks but your father's eyes, just as your father before you.'

He lets go and I sink back into my seat. He talks of my scourging but does not dwell on it, asking instead of my work, my education, my aspirations. I tell him, and he listens, picking up the doubts and hesitation as I speak. He knows. My father wishes me to follow in his footsteps and I think that I want this, too, but my grandfather can see the reluctance in my heart that I cannot.

'You have your father's eyes and his spirit also, he would not listen to me and neither will you follow him. You must do as your father wishes, Josephes, and then he will see for himself, as I did, that the son is father to the man.'

The burdens of the eldest son.
In the foreground someone is stacking wooden boards, behind him another is shaking dust off a sheet. There is a good deal of industry going on around me and the smell of wood. I am in the workshop of Yeshua's father. I walk through to the other side, nodding to the tradesmen who look up as I pass. On the other side of the workshop is a yard which is used for storing and seasoning timber; beyond that are the parts of the building used as offices. There is a man working there who sees me approach and points to a gateway in a side wall and says, 'He's in there.' I follow his directions and open the door. I step through into another small yard which is used for recreation and so has been planted with shrubs and climbing plants.

In the corner is Yeshua sitting with his back to the wall and his eyes closed. When he hears the door he turns toward me: 'Josephes!' he smiles but I am unable to return his greeting for it would appear that I am quite distressed. He sees my expression and asks what the matter is. I sit on the bench next to him. It is our last day together; tomorrow he will return to Qumran and I will resume my studies at the Temple but this impending separation is not the cause of my distress. I am angry about something connected with my father. I want to be free. The expectations of the eldest son do not always sit comfortably on my shoulders. These feelings are common to us both: he feels unfairly burdened by destiny and I by birth.

During these times it has become something of a pattern in our relationship that when one of us is feeling trapped the other commiserates. When my anger is spent I look vacantly into the middle of the yard and soften into some sort of acceptance. No words are spoken we just sit quietly together for a few moments before we set off.

Josephes finishes his education at the Temple.
I am sitting alone on a stone bench, waiting. I am thinly bearded, a young man. I am waiting to be invited into an interview concerning my education. My father is already inside and the man with whom he is speaking is a close and trusted friend of his who has overseen my studies. Not all the scholars at the Temple had been sympathetic to me because of my closeness to my cousin so my father stepped in to ensure that I would receive the kind of guidance that would suit my personality and sensibilities.

In due course I am invited to join them. There is an empty chair and I take my place. My father gives me a brief resume of what they have discussed and includes within it his understanding of my progress, my strengths and weaknesses and my development. From time to time my mentor interjects to clarify or affirm a point. He is a kindly man with an excellent mind for whom I have developed a deep affection over the years, so it is not without some emotion that I listen to his appraisal. When he has finished my father tells me that they have decided that my education at the Temple is now complete, that I will no longer have to attend classes or work with the tutors at home. He explains that now I am a man, as reasonably educated as any and able to take up more fully my duties as eldest son within the family.

As I listen I am surprised by how deeply affected I am by what is being said and, despite my best attempts to contain it, the welling of emotion turns to tears. This man so clearly recognises the difficulty of my situation. My education at the Temple was at my father's instigation. He wanted me so much to follow him and join the Sanhedrin that he has been perhaps a little blind to my unsuitability for such a path.

For months I have felt torn between my father's wishes and my own identity. My tutor recognised this, he recognised my devotion to my cousin and he also recognised the potential within me. Through his compassion, understanding and encouragement over the years I have learned to accept my own skills and abilities and have developed a love of philosophy, law, languages and history.

He has been a true teacher, one who never separated knowledge from the knower, who could see the point at which to make a suggestion for further study without imposing it, whose eyes sparkled when he taught and who was able to bring out the best in his students through the careful application of love and discipline in turn. Now it is he who is explaining to my father that my future lies elsewhere, it is he who is giving my life and destiny back into my own hands.

I feel such a very deep gratitude to him and stumble over my words in trying to express my feelings. It is not needed however, for when I look up there is clearly great feeling in his eyes, too. It is a difficult parting. We take our leave and my father walks with me, his hand on my shoulder, into the brilliant sunshine in the street.

Josephes' conflict between his love for his father and his own wishes.

Bright moonlight. It is cold and I am alone, sitting with my back to a rock looking at the enormous star-lit desert sky. I am depressed or grieving, it is difficult to tell which, possibly a bit of both. There are times when I feel that my life is not what my family had hoped for, that I am a disappointment to my father. He had high hopes for me and although he never insists that they are met if they conflict with my own interests, it is still a burden for he is a powerful man. It would probably be easier if I knew more clearly what I wanted from life but I do not. I am just different from him and sometimes that is hard for either of us to recognise. Leaving the Temple today was a relief for me because the studying was Father's desire, not mine, and now that relief has turned to darker feelings for it would seem sometimes that my delight is his disappointment. To rebel is one thing, but to have responsibility for my own life is not as comforting as I thought it would be, now that I am responsible for the consequences of my own choices. My father's love is far more important to me than I ever dare admit, even to myself, and so I try to do what he wants, but I cannot go against my nature.

The son of his father but not his father's son.

It is no easy thing being surrounded by those with such a powerful calling, to be caught in such a time as this. To say that I feel inadequate this night would not be entirely true. I know that if were only the normal course of events in the life of a nobleman's son that I had to deal with, I would be more than adequate to the tasks, but that is not the case. I sense history being made all around me, portentous events and visions, not from some ancient sage or distant priest but from those within my own family, my own cousin and those who are my dearest friends.

I know that those of whom I speak love me deeply but tonight my capacity for feeling that love is limited, and what is worse I feel that I have failed my father, who has put so much hope and faith in me. I cannot be him, nor his hopes. He thinks in grand schemes, he studies the prophets, he has his eye on a golden future, but I have little interest in these things and the difference that is so apparent this night gives me cause to reflect on my own capacities. It is dangerous ground, for to be different is to be alone.

It is my deepest fear that my love is too humble, too much about feelings and without real substance. I cover it up with talk and with strength but in truth it is the people in my life that I care about, the individuals, their lives, their worries and their hopes, not the patterns or schemes that they fit into and to my shame this night such simplicity gives me cause for sorrow.

The dawn comes slowly. I have been up all night and am stiff and cold but with the grey light of dawn comes a new resolve, a deeper acceptance of who I am, or more accurately who I am not. I am too tired from thinking to pity myself any longer so I get up painfully and start the walk home. It is a strange feeling that I walk with, difficult to describe: I feel both empty and at peace. What brought me to this place seems insignificant now. I am the son of my father but I am not my father's son.

Josephes takes charge and sells some minerals.
The night sky, the desert. The ground is visible, star-lit, it is very cold. I am dressed warmly and looking out into the night sky. Behind me are others and we have camped here for the night. There is a small fire, the horses are tethered to rocks, I can hear them moving and breathing but I am captivated by the purity and clarity of the desert air.

I am the senior member on this trip and it is the first time that such a trust has been placed in me. Amongst my travelling companions are my younger brother and my father's servant, Abu. There is a tacit agreement between us that if anything does go badly wrong he will take charge and protect the group, but he is both loyal and discreet and allows me my head. He stands in a unique position within the family; he is in charge of all the servants, most of whom are Nubian like him, but some are Egyptian. Such is the love between him and my father that he carries my father's proxy, and the love that is returned to him by the family is such that none dispute it.

There are limits to this, however, for he makes no business decisions and it is in this area that my own skills are being nurtured by this trip. It is an indulgence in one way, for I am to do business with another trusted friend of my father, who I know will not drive too hard a bargain, but it is a necessary indulgence for this is the way that the sons of businessmen are encouraged to take on responsibility for the family affairs.

It is morning and we are moving on, packing up our camp. In the desert it is important to start as early as possible in order to take advantage of the cool air whilst travelling. There is also always the danger of bandits but they typically prey on the weak or the solitary and leave parties on horseback such as ourselves alone.

Before long we are on our way, riding through the arid rocky gorges that traverse this area. Wherever there is a choice of direction or path, Abu waits for my decision before proceeding even though there is no comparison between his experience of travelling in these parts and my own. If I were to make a very poor choice he would advise me but it is my goal on this trip that he will not find cause. In this way he will maintain the overall protection of the party while I will learn from his experience by trying to emulate it. It is a good training.

When we finally arrive at the settlement we have been making for it is late afternoon. Abu and I unsaddle the horses and he gives his approval of my conduct during the day. His words are more valuable than gold to me and what I will only appreciate later in life is that his example is priceless. Few men can quietly stand by and watch those younger and less experienced than themselves learn from their mistakes, but he is one. He knows that boys become men not through competition and dominance but through the encouragement of those they admire and a guiding hand at their backs.

There is a river, and women washing cloth in it. They pound the cloth against rocks and then two of them take a corner each and open it up in the water to allow the current to gently unfurl the creases so it billows slowly in the stream. In the foreground a man is pounding something in a tub with a large pestle. I draw closer and see that the tub is full of cloth and dye stuff, a deep blue-black. I look up and all around me are coloured cloths drying in the hot sun.

The settlement we have come to is concerned with the dying of cloth. They have found a home next to the river so that they can make use of the plentiful supply of water required for their trade. I am being shown round by one of the elders. We have come here because he wants to know if we can supply the minerals from which he makes his dyes. I examine the quality of his existing stock and we discuss the costs of the materials he needs. He is agreeable and we make a bargain.

During these proceedings Abu has kept a discreet distance but now that the business part of the proceedings is over he joins us with the other members of the party for refreshments.

Late at the synagogue.
I am running towards a building, headcloth and toga billowing out behind me. I am a young man, bearded, with sandals on my feet. I reach the building and pause for a moment to catch my breath, leaning against the wall. The building is a synagogue and I am late for the service. The family are already assembled inside and I know that they will be wondering where I am. I straighten my clothing and walk as quietly as possible into the gloom of the temple. As my eyes adjust to the light I can see my father

looking over his shoulder to see that I am safely inside. I make my way through those assembled and take my place by his left side. I feel his hand on my arm through my tunic. There is no recrimination for my being late, just appreciation that I am here.

Josephes at ease with his mother.
My mother is sitting at a table in the Jerusalem home. Behind her through an open window I can see the scattered dwellings of the outskirts of the city and the hills beyond. On the table in front of her is a slab of grey wet clay which she is moulding. The room that we are in is high up in the house and has been set aside exclusively for this purpose.

She works the clay deftly, the grey drying to white on her wrists and forearms. Her hands express her feelings as we talk, sometimes smoothing and caressing the clay and at other times punching and gouging. We spend many hours together in this way, me half-sitting on a bench against the wall and she at her modelling.

Sometimes I join her and take a piece of clay to mould. I have some talent in this direction but have never really developed it as she has. There is and always has been an ease between us, an understanding that makes the passing of time together a pleasure.

Josephes compares himself with his younger brother.
I am with Eliazar, my younger brother at the Jerusalem home. It is rare that we spend time together these days. He is very strict with himself, and we are totally unlike each other, even in the way that we dress. He is fastidious in every way, his attitudes are serious and devout and he takes on causes in a very total way. His nature is one of self-denial where mine is more one of pleasure. He is quiet and introverted where I am extrovert and gregarious. I wish he would ease up on himself a little more; when I look into his eyes he seems so far away.

Perhaps I envy my brother a little. He seems to me to

be hardly in the world, ethereal and spiritual compared to my more earthy attributes. But I have my positive qualities. I have a good heart, a genuine love of people and I will always help wherever I can. I try always to fulfil what is expected of me and do not shirk my responsibilities whereas he seems not to get involved in them in the first place. My goal is always to do that which I have said I will do, where he promises nothing. I am the very opposite of my brother, who stands back from action and underestimates rather than overestimates his ability.

Josephes visits his old teacher.
A group of low buildings. They are official or institutional in nature and consist of one main hall that has been added to over the years with different rooms and annexes. Each addition is built in a slightly different style or has a different roof height giving the whole thing an interesting and pleasantly jumbled appearance. I approach the building and enter through double doors which stand open. There is a paved courtyard inside with a well and some plants growing against the walls. I know where I am going and make my way to the left of the yard where there is a windowed room. I knock on the door and wait.

The door is opened by an old man who bids me enter. He is not the man I have come to visit, he is a servant who ushers me into a study. There are scrolls on shelves and a writing desk. The man I have come to see belongs to a community of scholars who are housed in this complex. Like the man who answered the door he is dressed simply in white cotton. He rises when I enter, bids me welcome, resumes his position and then looks up and gives me his full attention.

It is some time since I have given up my studies at the Temple and been released from my father's wish that I follow his footsteps into the Sanhedrin. This man, who was my teacher then, has continued to take an interest in my progress in life even though he has no responsibility for my education, and for this I am extremely grateful. I have always felt that he understood me and his understanding is a great solace to me. He is someone who knows that it is not just the role in life that is important but the person who enacts that role. With so many around me of extraordinary power or gifts it is often very difficult for me to give value to my contribution, but this man sees beyond the superficial to the deeper person, the one who is unaffected by circumstance.

To talk with him always brings an understanding and a gladness to my heart. To read the laws of the Jews or the teaching of the Essenes without experience of the ways of those who have attempted to follow them brings scant understanding of what they mean in reality. There are fanatics, of course, who insist that the letter of the law be followed and the nature of the Hebrew language requires a precise formulation for the writer to convey what is intended into writing. But my mentor is not one such as these; he follows the laws seriously and lives by them. He understands that the laws are set down not as facts but as guidelines to a more wholesome life that reflects a divine purpose rather than as a set of rules to live by, and this is why I seek him out.

Josephes bringing Yeshua back from Qumran.
We are approaching Qumran. I am with a group of fellow travellers who have been sent to bring Yeshua back to Jerusalem. It is hot, approaching the middle of the day and we are tired from the journey. There is an understanding within the household of the needs of younger members, not just my brother, my sister and myself but all those who are young. In terms of moral education here is little difference between the treatment of the offspring of servants and the offspring of the head of the house. All are disciplined and encouraged alike, and all have been encouraged to respect their elders. In young adulthood this respect is rewarded with responsibility, so when we arrive at Qumran the older members of the party, knowing how important it

is to me, step back and allow me go and fetch my cousin.

What is so extraordinary about our meeting is that it is so ordinary, the time that has separated us ceases to exist as soon as we see each other. Conversations that were left in mid-sentence at our last meeting are started once again, and there is an excited torrent of news, argument and relief that lasts several hours.

Perhaps it is only in later life that people need to convert their feelings into words before they can be understood, but there is also an intensity in what is unsaid. All the things that vocabulary cannot capture weight the atmosphere. What words can describe the familiarity that exists between friends? What phrase can capture the ease and confidence of knowing another person as well as one's self? And what science can render the alchemy of love into the elements from which it springs? It is better to allow these things to be ordinary, for that is what they are.

Josephes' father buys him a horse.
A market, or to be more precise, a horse-fair. There are traders of many nationalities here: Arab, Jew, Indian, Mongols. I am here with my father and Abu to buy a horse. It is before a trip to Egypt and my father has decided that it is time that I had a horse of my own. Abu is quite knowledgeable in the area of horses and so he has come along to offer his wisdom.

Each of the traders leads a horse in front of those who have come to buy. They walk the horse from right to left and then turn, mount and ride back with a flourish and a gallop. Many of those who breed these mounts are wild and proud men who know the value of what they are selling. I have my eye on a beautiful chestnut mare with a black mane and tail. It is not difficult to come to a choice for we all agree that she is the horse for me. My father and Abu approach the owner, a weather-beaten face with a blue turban and jacket over white tunic and trousers. He sees me and, immediately recognising that I have made up my mind, calls me over, hands me the rein and encourages me to mount. I do as I am bid, watched closely by the breeder, and when I am on her back I cannot help a broad grin spreading across my face. The owner looks up at me and informs me that the beast is of a gentle and obedient nature. This is all to the good for he has clearly observed from the way that I mounted her that I am not a natural horseman. Whilst I remain like a statue on her back my father falls to haggling over the price. I think that all realise that this is only a formality for, whatever the price may be, the horse and I will not be parted.

Josephes reflects on his role in life.
I am looking down at something made of leather – it is the pommel of a saddle. I am riding my horse, my back is sore and I can smell the sweat of the horse. It is quite hot. The horse and I have become firm companions. I look ahead and see my father, riding a magnificent black Arab stallion. He is swathed in a deep blue robe that is wound about his head and body and also covers and shades the horse's hindquarters. He stops briefly and turns to look back towards me. Behind me are others. I am a young man of perhaps eighteen or nineteen years old and we are on a journey to Egypt.

I have travelled extensively with my father both for the purposes of business and pleasure and this is a business trip. I have learned much of the business world by accompanying him on such trips and watching him work. There is nothing unusual about this; in fact I have met other young men, the sons of those with whom my father does business, who are in the same position as myself and who have become good friends. This is encouraged by the fathers since it is understood that the business concerns of the father will pass to the eldest son and in this way trading relations can be protected and kept within the same families for many generations to come.

This trip is especially memorable because it marks an opening of a new kind of relationship between my father and myself. The journey has necessitated travelling through desert and sparsely populated areas. At night we camp under the star-lit sky and talk for hours on many diverse subjects. He is a very educated man and has an opinion on most things but it is not so much the breadth of his education that I like as the depth of his reflection. His opinions are invariably his own rather than those that have been learned and repeated. I admire him greatly and even though I sometimes feel that I will never be able to do with my life what he has done with his, I have modelled myself on him in the best way that I can.

We are riding past the Pyramids. They appear ahead of us, shimmering in the desert heat. The road leads past them and curves to the right so we pass them on our left-hand side. They are so far away that it takes us the best part of the morning to ride past them and on to the city.

It is the custom to dismount and lead the horses by hand in the towns and this we do. My father's servant takes his horse and leads the way whilst my father walks along-side me. We make our way to the home of the nobleman with whom we will be staying. He lives in a villa near the densely populated centre of the city. The streets are narrow and crowded and the houses are cheek by jowl with each other. From the outside the villa looks nothing special: high yellowish walls stained with the passage of time and traffic. When we arrive servants take our horses into a walled and gated yard adjacent to the main house and we are ushered through the yard and into the villa.

There is no comparison between the outside of the villa and the inside – it is breathtaking, an oasis of beauty and tranquillity. The main building is on two storeys around a central courtyard. The upper rooms are connected by a balustraded covered walkway on the first floor which in parts is festooned with richly scented flowering vine. In the centre of the intricately paved courtyard is a lush garden set about a fountain.

Our host greets us and welcomes my father effusively,

while on the first floor his wife and younger children call down to us. The nobleman turns his attention to me and admires my stature, then calls for his own son who is called Alex or Alexander. Alex arrives and grins at me in a slightly conspiratorial manner. We have spent time together before and made a firm friendship when our family was resident in Egypt and again on the occasions when his father and he were guests at our Jerusalem home. Soon we are seated and eating around a table in a shady corner of the court-yard and the air is filled with the sound of conversation and laughter and in the background, the delightful trickling of the fountain.

Alex and I are alone; it is night-time, and our families are still talking. Alex has a reckless quality and an enthusiasm for life in him which I admire. He and his family are traders, they are Jews but have settled in Egypt. We have slipped away to the stables. Alex has a great interest in horses and their care. He has introduced me to his beloved charges and we are now in a small room adjacent to the stables. He asks for news of my cousin and other members of the family and I tell him of the events and adventures that we have had since he last stayed at our home. It is an earnest exchange. He wants to know if I have been with a woman since our last meeting. Thankfully he senses my embarrassment at being asked and instead of insisting on an answer describes in great detail and with great relish his own adventures in that department of life.

Alex and I are riding through the desert towards the Pyramids. Each of us wears the long robe necessary for protection from the sun in the desert and we each carry a goat-skin full of water that is so important for ourselves and our horses. Alex is an excellent rider, he knows the desert hereabouts and the limitations of his mount. Although we are headed toward the Pyramids our destination lies beyond them, a smaller tomb that I have asked to visit.

The Pyramids are deceptive landmarks. Their scale is so large that it is easy to think that they are smaller than they are in reality and therefore assume that we are closer than we actually are. Many travellers have fallen foul of that illusion. It is a long ride past them but eventually we reach our destination. It is the same tomb that Yeshua and I visited when still in our infancy and residing in Egypt to escape the attentions of Herod. For some reason or other the memory of the trip to the tomb has always remained as fresh in my mind and the picture has never faded, so now I am in Egypt again I have persuaded Alex to bring me out here today to satisfy my curiosity.

We enter the tomb and like so many things first visited in childhood it seems smaller than I remember it; otherwise my memory has remained faithful. Alex, although known to us during our stay in Egypt, was younger than I and so had not accompanied us on that first trip. As we enter I describe my memory to him in detail. He is able to interpret some of the hieroglyphs and pictures for me as his education has taken in a study of Egyptian history and ancient writings.

My feelings while in this tomb are hard to describe: it seems so long ago that I was here and yet there is also a feeling of time having stood still. We stand in silence looking around and drinking in the atmosphere and mystery, there is an air of the ancient but also of abandonment and dereliction. Alex interrupts my reverie to ask what I am thinking. I tell him and he nods slowly, but I do not think that he really understands, it was the ride that was important for him, not the destination. There is a little discomfort between us; he is bored and wants to get going but I want to stay a little longer. We compromise: he will prepare the horses for the return journey whilst I stay for a few more minutes in the tomb by myself.

I trace my fingers along the carvings. There is something that I want from this place before I leave but I don't know what it is. My mind wanders; these are troubled times for me, it is hard for me to understand the part I play in the family, surrounded by the rich and powerful, not just materially but also in terms of talent. I often feel that I don't really have a role to play and such feelings can on occasion lead to quite severe depression and questioning. I wonder if I will ever understand my part in this drama. As the question crystallises in my mind the answer comes quite clearly: 'You will, Josephes, you will.'

I immediately feel a peace descend and I am reassured in a way that cannot be attributed to the hearing of the words alone, and I am also overtaken by a deep awareness that I am playing my part and it is a part that only I can play. It is as if the ancient occupier of this place has answered me himself.

It is night-time and I am exhausted. We have stabled the horses and I am making my way to my room. On the way I pass my father's door; there is a light on so I call out to him. He is sitting quietly in a chair wearing a loose white cotton tunic, reading from one of his beloved scrolls. He smiles as he sees me and enquires whether I found what I was looking for. I reply that I did. He must sense a change in me because he adds that he feels a great peace in my heart since then.

It is only when he says it that I realise how content I have been since my experience in the tomb, how easily the conversation flowed between Alex and myself on the ride home and how unconcerned for the past and future I have been. I wish my father good night and as I make my way to my room realise again that he probably knows me a great deal better that I give him credit for.

Another trip to Egypt.
We have come again with my father to Egypt, this time with Yeshua. The purpose of this visit is to further our education. My father not only oversees my education and that of my brother and sister but also that of Yeshua and other of the young people in the family. This has

trips to Greece as well as Egypt, but it is to Egypt that we are drawn more often. On this occasion Yeshua and I are young men, and we are familiar with the terrain and with many of the people who dwell here from our soujorn in this country as youngsters.

My father has organised the formal part of our trip which is largely the exploration of certain tombs. On these trips we take others who are expert in deciphering pictures that adorn the walls, and it is the information contained within these pictures that we are instructed to commit to memory. This is much easier for Yeshua than for myself as he is gifted with almost total recall. Whether or not he can understand the pictures is irrelevant, he seems to be able to understand the intent behind them. Over the years it has become apparent that he is extremely gifted in many areas: his ability to heal, his memory, his ability to under-stand are supreme but on this occasion he demonstrates an ability for interpretation that astounds even the experts that guide us. He has the gift of being able to go to the very heart of the matter. This has always been true in his dealings with people but here he shows the same gift applied to ancient writings, writings that he has never been trained to read.

My father is very concerned about which tombs we enter. He takes the view that they have power, that some are welcoming and some are not. He is quite strict on this point but we are not quite so strict.

I can see a dark triangle in the sand. That is all that is visible of the tomb, just an opening. We have come here to explore without my father, while he is attending to busi-ness matters. We slide down into the hole and enter into the darkness. We are both surprised: we had expected a humble tomb but this one is quite vast with many cham-bers. We have a small oil lamp and proceed from one room to another, our feet soft on the floor. Yeshua's attention is taken by one wall in particular that is covered in hiero-glyphs. He stands gazing at it, concentrating, his lips moving slightly as he scans the pictures. Finally he turns to me and says, 'This man was a great teacher, but there are strange things written here. They were a truly great civilisation, they knew things that are beyond our imagination.'

He continues scanning the pictures then stops and looks away, he is clearly a little stunned by what he has read and says 'Josephes, I have just read about myself.' He points to a small section and explains the text. I cannot really comprehend what he is saying, for how could the builders of this tomb have known about Yeshua over two thousand years ago? I put the question to him and he replies enigmatically, ' I don't know, they did, that's all, they just knew.'

It is evening and we are sharing a meal with my father. Yeshua is explaining to him what we found. I half expect him to be angry but he is tolerant. I think that he has given up expecting Yeshua to conform to the dictates of a normal education. He says that it would perhaps have been better had we not entered that particular tomb, but at the same time is fascinated by Yeshua's understanding of what he has seen. Much of the discussion concerns the origins of the Egyptians, where they came from and of a vast and ancient civilisation that virtually destroyed itself.

My father talks quietly of history and how it repeats itself, of how teachers come from time to time to help us learn from the past and to gain a deeper understanding of the will of God. He says that teachers such as these are precious and almost always experience persecution by the authorities. He says that the tomb we visited today was the burial place of one such as this. He is enigmatic as he talks and will not be drawn further on the subject. He retires to bed, leaving us to ponder his words.

Chapter 5

As an adult

It is sunrise in the desert. I have been awake for some hours waiting for this. I watched the stars give way to the grey light of dawn and then the yellow light on the eastern horizon grow more intense until the sun cast long shadows around me. Now I can feel the warmth of the sun on my face. I love the peace of this place and often come here to think and to be alone.

Family life.
I can see an olive tree from a distance and sitting in its shade is a woman. She is working, intent upon what she is doing – sewing I think. I watch from a distance: there is an air of solitude about her, she seems sad or resigned as she works. She looks up, sees me and brightens up as I approach her and sit down next to her. It is Rachel, my elder sister and she is embroidering a shawl. There is an affection between us but not as strong as her love for her father; to her he is the sun in the sky. The shawl is for him.

A business transaction concluded.
There is a tent being erected, a stake being banged into the ground to anchor the tent. There are preparations. A lamb has been killed and I can see its forelegs tied together. There is blood on the cord. We are in the desert, with Arab people, and there will be a meal tonight that is going to be held in my honour. I can hear cloth flapping in the breeze. Some of the men are dressing in long red trousers, naked from the waist up: they are entertainers.

I am here to trade with these people. They are transporters and I have come to procure their services for the the carriage of goods across the desert. Their leader is known to my father. He is warm and generous, I like him and I sense that the feeling is mutual. We are able to make a good deal. The sky is beautiful and I stay as their guest for the night.

An important feast day.
It is a great feast, the most important in the Jewish calendar, and the Jerusalem home and garden are full to capacity. With all the children there must be almost one hundred people assembled here. As the eldest son I enjoy my privilege to the full on these occasions. As I have grown older my father has become more tolerant of me and how I use my position, as his father became of him. My status and warmth at these events attracts a great deal of attention. It enables me to show openness, generosity, humour and grace and I spend the day with my family and friends talking, drinking and laughing.

Josephes and Yeshua meet again.
I am looking down the side of a building, an entrance way in the wall opens on to a workshop, a carpentry workshop. There are ten or fifteen men working here, sawing, planing and carving the components to make furniture. The business is owned by Yeshua's father, although due to his advanced age Yeshua's elder stepbrothers do most of the practical work of running the business.

It had been Joseph's wish that Yeshua himself would one day take over the business but Yeshua, being a young man who has only ever done that which is aligned with his own sense of purpose, has never shown the slightest interest in so doing, although he has always shown great interest in the craftsmen who are employed here. Also he has an abhorrence of physical labour, not because he is too proud but because he will do nothing that will damage his hands. He has long since accepted his abilities as a healer and feels that his hands represent this gift and that they should be reserved for healing alone. As a child and even to this day it has always been Yeshua's delight to be in nature and he is renowned for disappearing for days at a time either alone or with myself or another for company, into the desert or hills that surround the city.

On this day I have arranged to meet him here because it is mutually convenient to us both. I can see him now coming through the workshop towards me, smiling and returning the calls of the men he passes. We set off briskly towards the outskirts of town.

It is still morning and the air is cool. After a while we reach a shaded and grassy olive grove which overlooks the city. We spent many hours here together when we were younger and it is only when we are seated that we relax and start to talk earnestly. We are young men now and childhood is long past. We lie back propped on our elbows breathing the fresh air as if for the first time. There is nothing of great importance that passes between us in our conversation, just a reacquainting, sharing news and chatting about what each of us has been doing.

The power of moonlight.
We two are alone. I am standing by his right shoulder. It is night-time, early night-time. A full moon hangs low over the sea. His face is turned away from me towards the moon. We spend a few minutes like this in silence, just contemplating the view before us. It is he who speaks first: 'How forgiving the moon is. Whatever the foolishness of man she still bathes him in her soft light. She has watched dynasties come and go and when the last fool stands alone on this land she will forgive even him.'

A little magic.
It is dark. I can just see Yeshua. He describes a circle with his hands, then uses his hands to give it depth, like an orb. He works on it as if he were polishing an imaginary sphere that is suspended in the air, level with his chest. Very gradually as he works, there appears a faint outline of the sphere in a silvery-grey, phosphorescent light. As he strokes the outline, the light becomes a little stronger. Then he stops and rests his hands by his sides, the sphere fades before our eyes as gradually as it appeared, until finally it is gone completely.

It is a side of Yeshua that few see, for he has an innate understanding of magic, not the magic of conjurers but of true magic, the ability to create and manifest. It is a skill that in later life he will have to give up for it is akin to the seduction of power and possessions. He will have to put his faith in love and nothing else.

Josephes contemplates his family responsibilities.
I see the family home: so many are living here, so many children all under one roof, one enormous family of three generations. When Father is away it falls to me to make the decisions about the running of the household and this is acknowledged by those present. The children, though, do not care who is who, to them all the adults are as important as each other and they relate to each one equally. It often falls to me to say a stern word when they are out of hand and to which they listen.

There are servants as well and always people staying or leaving, and decisions to be made about business matters. There is a respect for this family in the locality and people know who we are. There is a certain acknowledgement that is afforded to our position within the society. Father has a standing and power both in the religious and business aspects of life and this commands respect. As his elder son my position is also respected both within and outside the family and I enjoy the prestige that this brings. I do question this from time to time, feeling that were it not for being first-born son to my father I may not have sufficient inner resource to command such a position. It is hard to better such a man and find a standing in the community based on my own endeavours but nobody questions this except me, for it is the way with every father and son that the son carries on the position of the father. I have however made some progress in the world of business and the fact that this is noted brings satisfaction.

Josephes observes a Jewish tradition.
The great Temple at Jerusalem. I am sitting on the hot steps in the brilliant sunshine leaning back on my elbows. With me are two friends and we are talking. There are

similar groups to ours scattered all around the steps, as the Temple is not only a popular meeting place but also a place where those interested in spiritual matters meet and debate. On certain days the Temple steps become a sort of open school for religion and opinion and today is one of these days.

On this particular day a box containing scrolls will be carried out of the Temple. It is tradition that scrolls are prepared and blessed in the Temple before being transported to one of the lesser temples or synagogues. When it is a large or auspicious synagogue the scrolls are carried in a procession with the container slung between two poles which are borne by four of the party, usually members of the community for which the scrolls are bound.

As we sit, one such party begins its slow journey home and we watch as the bearers and their attendants make their way carefully down the steps. The word goes out from the source and thus the traditions of our people are kept alive.

We talk as they pass, about our religious beliefs, our families and our responsibilities. I know these two young men very well; we grew up together, but as we have grown into manhood tensions have developed, unspoken but there none the less. Much of the tension stems from the loss of equality between us. As they have grown they have had to take on the yoke of responsibility within their families as I have, but they have not been given anything like the same freedom or access to wealth. This leads to both admiration and envy.

It is not just freedom of action that I have, though, it is freedom of thought. The Arimathean family is singular in this respect. As children we were encouraged to question and to challenge those things that we did not agree with and thus to discover for ourselves that which we valued. In some ways this opportunity was not as welcome to my brother and sister as it was to me. They both seem to function better when the expectations are clear. In my case I relished the latitude afforded me, just as now I relish the chance to impress through debate.

Paying tribute to Caesar.

I am walking through the city. Three of us arrive at a large and impressive building and pause for a moment. I have been accompanied here for my protection. Over the shoulder of one of the group I can see two Roman soldiers standing guard at a large gateway. As we talk I study their movements; they are wearing leather breastplates, short tunics and carry short swords and long spears. We are some distance away so they are not particularly aware of us. Occasionally one crosses the gateway to speak to the other. I leave my companions and approach them. They are both strong men, not boys, strong and fit.

I have mixed feelings as I approach: I dislike the Romans but I dislike the feeling in myself that wants to appease them even more. When it becomes clear to them that I am approaching their gateway they adopt more formal and guarded postures. The elder of the two addresses me in reasonable Aramaic and asks, 'What is your business, friend?' I explain that I wish to see a particular official. He steps back and bangs on the door; in a few moments it opens and a man looks out. The guard explains my request and calls over to ask my name. I give it and the door shuts. He points to the ground with the butt of his spear several yards from the door and says, 'Wait there.'

As I stand in the sun I remember the beating I received from these people many years earlier. I did not want to admit it at the time but that experience affected my attitude to the Romans profoundly. They were the agents of humiliation and it is still hard for me to separate the beating from the lesson that I learned. The net result of all this is quite a deep confusion in my feelings towards them. I hate the fact that I felt pleased when the guard addressed me as friend.

In due course the door opens again, the same man

speaks to the guard and gestures towards me. The guard beckons me over and I follow the man through the door. He is an older man, a minor official, perhaps fifty years old, slight in build, grey and balding wearing a white toga. He walks quickly down the cloistered side of a courtyard and we enter through a door and into a hallway opposite the main entrance.

It is cool inside, with a flagstone floor. To one side of the hallway stand double doors with an impressive architrave around them. My guide knocks on the door, opens it and announces my arrival then bids me enter. The room is grand in proportion although sparsely furnished. The walls are bare stone hung with rich draperies and there is a mosaic floor and high ceiling. The furnishings consist of two desks and several chairs. Behind the main desk sits the man I have come to see. He bids me sit in flawless Greek.

He is a cultured man with the ease of manner that high office affords. He asks after my father and my family and I share the same pleasantries with him. I hear the door open behind me but do not look up. The man who entered waits patiently beside the second desk until we have finished our conversation. At an opportune moment I reach to my belt and lift a heavy purse of gold coins, the standing man steps forward and takes the purse from me, then proceeds to count the contents on the second desk while we continue our conversation. There is a small fortune in that purse.

When he is finished he makes an entry into his ledger and hands me back the empty purse and a tally; he nods to my host who smiles at me and wishes me well. It has been a dignified and congenial transaction. Whatever the true feelings of the parties involved, they have been well hidden on this occasion. I bid him farewell, leave the room and meet my escort who leads me from the building.

This is how the Arimathean family pay taxes to the Romans; this is how we fill Caesar's coffers, and in return Caesar helps us fill ours.

Josephes gives alms.

I am walking through the busy streets of Jerusalem alone, through the bright lights and dark shadows of midday. I am feeling happy, stopping as I walk to talk to people I know. I walk down a long flight of steps near the Temple. They are fully exposed to the heat of the sun and I feel glad that I am walking down them rather than up.

At the base of the Temple there is a poor district and this is where I am headed. The streets are narrow and dirty, like the children that play in them and follow me, pulling at my cloak asking for small coins. I turn abruptly down a narrow alleyway and walk towards a single-room dwelling at the opposite end. On the steps is an old woman soaking her feet in a bowl of water. She nods as I approach and moves sideways so that I can get to the door. I knock and it is opened by a man about the same age as myself. He greets me effusively and introduces me to the old woman who he says has come to borrow his bowl. She looks up at me with a toothless smile on her face and I smile back. We go inside. I know this man very well. He is neither priest nor one of these people but he has made both them and the true obligation of the priesthood his own. He lives amongst them, loves them and gives what he can to them. He tries in his own way to relieve their suffering.

I have brought alms for him, alms from our family that have never been asked for and are never refused. I bring them to help him in his work, but I know that it is not the money that makes a difference to the people he helps. It is his simplicity, his ready smile and open hand, for he is not sophisticated in any way. He has known suffering, more than most, but it has not caused him to retreat, just to understand more. He is a good man, pure and simple, and that goodness touches the hearts of all, rich and poor alike.

Josephes' action to widen a gate in the city wall ends in humiliation.

I can see the full moon out of the open window of our

Jerusalem home. The light is like day, catching on the sleeve of my father's robe as he rests his arm on the table. There are no lanterns lit in the room, the moon provides ample light to see by. My father is just returned from a business trip abroad. He has rested and bathed and now we are discussing the events that have passed whilst he has been away.

He tells me of his travels and the business commitments that he has made, although not in the same detail as he expects me to account to him. It is difficult. While he is away I am head of the household, when he returns he is the head of the household; I have no argument with this, it is as it should be. The struggle that I have is that the role of head carries power. When I am head of the household I have the same power, the same responsibility as he does. The problem is that I feel that I do not have the same authority. With his own father he had to earn his right to be the head, his father was strict, while more recently he gives me the freedom to find my own path. Too much freedom perhaps, so I try to follow his example and be like him at the same time as doing things differently so that I can be like myself.

On this occasion I am explaining to my father about the wall. While he was away I responded to several urgent requests that one of the narrow gates in the city wall be widened to permit easier passage by the tradesmen and transporters of goods that use it. To be a member of the Sanhedrin requires not only great learning but also great wealth, for the members are responsible for maintaining the fabric of certain parts of the city and in particular the protective wall. The section of the wall in question was one that my father, and in his absence I, was responsible for. I knew that my father had been meaning to put the work in hand for several years so I took steps to see that the work was carried out.

Once again my actions earned me censure by the Sanhedrin. The work, they claimed, was being done at the wrong time of year, with the wrong materials and with the wrong artisans. They made me stop the work until my father returned, and in the interim the partly demolished section of the wall has stood as a rather humiliating monument to their disapproval of my actions...

Now I am listening to my father. He says that he knows that I meant well but to mean well is not enough. Each member of the Sanhedrin acts on behalf of the others, so as the son acting on behalf of a member I must ensure that my actions are in accordance with their wishes. I could have asked any one of them for advice and I should not be too arrogant to do so.

In fact he is not as angry as he could have been, more exasperated than angry. Perhaps he realises that my pride has already suffered, even though I will not admit it. But such is the nature of pride: the dread of being exposed, ridiculed, of being found to be less, or motivated by envy or ambition, the fear that I am not the man I seek to depict. These are the terrible fears that assail me, and do we not all attract to us the very things we fear?

Josephes and Yeshua clash with the authorities for very different reasons.
I am walking with my cousin. As we have grown from boyhood to manhood each of us has had his share of clashing with the authorities. He, too, has been branded as arrogant but for different reasons than me. Where it is felt that my actions are in need of discipline, it is more his ideas that are considered wayward. I have been accused of wanting to be too much like him and perhaps this is true but it does not take away from our friendship.

A no-go area and a new friend.
I am dazed. I open my eyes and realise that I am on the ground looking along a gutter in the middle of an alleyway. There is a trickle of water in the gutter and my cheek

is in the water. I have just been violently attacked and knocked to the ground. I start to get up but am kicked viciously in the stomach and fall down again. I look up and see men, their headcloths drawn tightly around their faces. There are three of them and they are yelling at me. I cannot understand what they are saying and our discussion does not develop any further as the sound of approaching footsteps causes them to give up their task and flee.

A man rounds the corner and immediately comes to my aid. I do not know him: he is about ten years older than me and from his dress he is not particularly wealthy but he is solicitous and concerned as he helps me to my feet. He wants to know what has befallen me but I am at a loss to tell him. The side of my face is bruised and my right eye is starting to close. Suddenly I feel very weak and have to put my arm on his shoulder to steady myself. He takes command of the situation and leads me to his home which is close by.

His room is simple and I feel safe. He brings fresh water to wash my face and offers me tea which I accept gratefully. It stings but it washes the blood from the inside of my mouth. The combination of the tea and the safety of his home makes me feel much better, and I am able to focus my attention on him. He is strong in body but with a gentle and sensitive character. He asks nothing so I introduce myself, and he nods in recognition and says that he knows of my father and has heard of me. He sees me looking at his hands which are rough from manual work and, telling me his name, explains that he is a stonemason. This explains his knowledge of my father who is a Mason – not of course one who works with his hands, but one who belongs to their society and who commissions work from time to time.

I am intrigued by my new friend. There is a quality of acceptance about him that is hard to describe; he makes no judgments and treats me as an equal. He explains that this is a part of the city where Jews are not welcome, especially those who look as if they may be wealthy. I knew that, but my strength has saved me from attack in the past. As he speaks, he motions toward my headcloth which I am holding in my hands. Although it is my habit to dress simply my headcloth is of coloured silk, a luxury that few from this area could afford.

Suddenly, as he is speaking, I remember why I came here and reach for the document I was carrying: it is safe under my belt. I explain my mission and he offers to accompany me the rest of the way so that I can deliver the letter safely. I gratefully accept, feeling no misgivings about doing so as it is clear that, despite having only just met, there is an affinity between us which I trust implicitly.

As we walk for the remainder of my errand we lapse easily into conversation. He tells me about his background and I tell him of mine. He is a spiritual man with many original views. His work as a stonemason has brought him into contact with many ancient teachings and he has travelled extensively through his work. He has also made pilgrimages to ancient sites and monuments. We share memories of Egypt and even of specific tombs that we have visited.

As we continue, it strikes me that it is as if I have known this man for a very long time, for our conversation is akin to that which two old friends who have not seen each other for years might have. I have grown accustomed to keeping my involvement with the teachings of Yeshua out of my conversations but once my letter has been securely delivered and we are nearing his home, I decide to invite him to meet my cousin. After all, it is Yeshua himself who has told us that we need not seek out those of true heart – they will present themselves to us.

I can see a small group gathered at the entrance to a building. I have brought my new friend to hear the teaching. We are still some way off when I see someone step out of the entrance and talk to the group, whereupon they disperse rapidly. He recognises me and bids us enter immediately and as we go in he explains that he asked them to go away and return in ones and twos lest they draw attention to the meeting. Once inside, we are amongst friends and settle down to wait for those who have been sent away to return and for Yeshua to arrive. Before long there are about fifteen or so in the room.

Without ceremony one of the latecomers removes his headcloth and reveals himself to be Yeshua; he entered so quietly that I did not notice him come in. He laughs at my surprise and then wastes no time, starting to talk immediately. My eyes are not so much on Yeshua as on my new friend. Since inviting him I had some misgivings about whether I had done the right thing and am anxious to see his reaction to what he is hearing. He watches so intently that it is hard for me to read his face. He senses me watching him and after a few moments turns to me and whispers, 'Your cousin is the most beautiful teacher I have ever heard in my life'; as he turns away I see that there are tears in his eyes. I turn my attention back to Yeshua: a simple man, speaking the language of ordinary men, but able to convey so much.

When the teaching is finished people start to disperse, some stopping to talk or embrace as they go. Yeshua comes over to where we are standing and speaks directly to my companion, 'So, my cousin was successful in his mission. In helping him deliver his message, you helped him deliver mine to you. You must come again, my friend.'

Simon accompanies Josephes on a business call.
It is very early in the morning, still dark, the house sleeps. I lie on my couch waiting for the grey light to seep in through the window. When there is enough light to see by I pull back the covers and rise. Quietly and quickly I make my way out of the room, downstairs and into the garden. It is still and cold. I pause and look up at the morning star before I wash from an urn set beside the wall of the house.

The water is freezing and startles me awake. I walk quietly down the garden to the small building where Simon sleeps. Simon although a servant is virtually a brother. My father adopted him into the family as a child and he has developed a gift for languages. I do not have to wake him; he is already waiting for me, dressed and ready to go.

We walk quickly away from Simon's dwelling. Although Simon and myself are of similar ages we are of quite different race, he being from Africa and very dark-skinned – a Nubian. We have become closer as we have grown up, sharing our confidences and concerns with each other. While he is like a brother our relationship is without some of the power struggles that exist between Eli and myself. Within the younger members of the Arimathean family there are few secrets and Simon, although nominally a servant, is as much a member of the family as anyone else. We walk through the market and quietly past those who are sleeping or just beginning to stir on the street. Since I was attacked Simon has accompanied me on all the errands that are to do with the family business. The company makes the long walks a pleasure and the conversations we have whilst on them are both broad and long.

We walk in silence until the sun comes up, illuminating the tops of the houses and tall buildings. The light and the warmth loosens our tongues and we chat. It is a fairly long walk and it is almost mid-morning by the time we arrive at our destination: a secluded walled villa on the outskirts of the town. We reach the gate and I knock. A servant arrives and lets us in. Simon is directed to wait with the other servants whilst I am led to the owner of the house. There is no tension in our separation; it is accepted. It is not all households that are as liberal as our own. In most the servants are expected to know their places and are treated very much as servants. Many servants, while not exactly kept against their will, stay only through feelings of inadequacy and fear of starvation. In some houses Simon would not even be permitted entry because of his race – to many Jews the Nubians are considered as being almost sub-human. In this house the servants are treated well and without prejudice, but still as servants.

When my business is over, I am led to Simon and we set off again on the long walk home. It is with some glee that we recommence our discourse, for the advantage of having been treated as master and servant is that we are now able to compare the servants' view of the goings-on in the house, which have been liberally shared with Simon, with that of the patriarch's view, which have had an equal airing with me.

Josephes cannot share Yeshua's burden.
It is dark and wet, late at night, and we are away from the main house. Yeshua is squatting, his elbows on his knees, hands on his head, looking down at the ground between his feet. I am tired and uncomfortable, we have been up for hours talking. Yeshua is given to these occasional periods of depression and melancholia.

During times such as this he pleads with my father, he pleads with his mother and with me and when none of us can help him, he loses his appetite for life, goes away somewhere deep inside and pleads with himself. It is difficult for me: his moods are infectious. Such is the nature of the relationship between us that each feels fully the feelings of the other. In fact because of this, and despite all that has been said, there is actually little to say. It has all been said and not for the first time.

Now we are at the core of the issue, that which cannot be changed. Again and again he tries to put down his burden; again and again he arrives at this unpalatable real-isation: it is his burden and it cannot be shared. He must pick it up, carry it, and carry it alone. If I could carry it for him I would willingly do so, but I cannot. All I can do is watch and wait until he finds the strength to continue. And all I can do is pick up my burden, alone.

Josephes visits an old friend.
I am in the city of Jerusalem. Above me and to my right is the Temple. I have walked down the long flight of stairs hewn in the rock in the brilliant sunlight and now I am at the bottom, peering into the shadow that is created by a large dusty white building. As my eyes adjust to the light I see what I am looking for: a small door set in the otherwise featureless wall. I approach the door and knock, and it is answered almost immediately by a servant who lets me in. It is cool and dark inside. He leads me down the passage to a courtyard where there are water, plants and flowers. I am approached by a slim, elegant man, he is a close friend and we greet one another warmly. He sends the servant away to fetch tea.

In the shade to one side of the courtyard there are low couches laid over with rugs and cushions as he bids me sit and the servant appears with hot mint tea. We spend a few moments blowing and sipping and then launch into conversation. My host is a young scholar and scribe. Like myself he is the eldest son of wealthy parents and we were both put forward for schooling with a view to entering the Sanhedrin. He chose to take his studies forward and I chose to leave but our friendship, cemented during this period, has remained firm. Since that time our differences have not affected our relationship – if anything they have enhanced it – and our discussions have benefited from the diversity of our experience.

In a way we are mirrors for one another, each one of us could easily be in the position of the other and we are each intrigued by what we are missing.

Josephes and his crippled friend.
I am in a room, sitting and looking out of an open window, enjoying the breeze that comes through it. The window is partially framed by a delicately carved screen of Arab design, which is old and broken in places but still retains its elegance. I look around the room: it is sparsely furnished, a single-room dwelling in what was once a large

and beautiful structure but is now a faded and decaying lodging-house. I am sitting at a low table and my host, a man of my own age, is preparing a drink for us. I watch the drinks as he brings them to the table, marvelling at how he does not spill them, for his body is twisted and he walks with a very pronounced limp. He sits down awkwardly, almost spilling the tea but not quite. He laughs and we start to talk.

He is not from Jerusalem but is the youngest son from a large family in the countryside. His condition rendered him of little use in the family farming business but his brothers recognised his intelligence and even though they were not of great wealth they paid the costs of his education. Perhaps it is this that is the strength of our friendship: he is loved deeply by his family. The fact that he is crippled would have caused others to turn from him, but in his case his disability has been the cause of even greater love. It gives him a security and confidence that is a delight to behold.

Josephes' wife.

I am in Cyprus, very close to a young woman. She is looking very deeply and intently into my eyes and I am looking just as intently into hers, which are a deep chestnut brown. She is in my arms and should not be, for she is betrothed by her family to another. I find her incredibly beautiful, with her long black curly hair tumbling down over brown shoulders. She is possessed of a child-like innocence that I can barely resist, but now there is the added complication that she is pressing herself urgently against my thigh.

I have never had much luck convincing my desires to conform to the dictates of our society, and have led by no means a chaste life but this is different. She is the daughter of a business associate and I am a guest in his house. I have watched her grow over the years and as she has grown our affection for one another has grown, too, and has deepened to love. Now the time of her marriage to a man she does not even know is nigh, a convenience between

two families for the purposes of securing a business relationship, and she can see a loveless life spread before her.

Her lips are sweet and soft on mine, and I surrender to my
desire.

I feel remorseful and responsible after our consummation.
Without the flame of lust to cast a warm glow on our
actions, things seem more stark and impossible. We talk
quietly and I try to persuade her that our love cannot be
realised in marriage, it must remain a secret. On this point
the views of her father and society agree. Love is not even
given consideration where marriage is concerned, and the
pursuit of it frequently ends in disgrace.

It is difficult for me; in our family we were taught to
follow our hearts, but our society demands that we put the
needs of our families first when conducting our relationships. I, unlike so many others of my kind, was not
betrothed at birth. Because of this, most eligible women
have been unavailable to me because they were betrothed.

On my journey home I am not sure whether to regret
my actions or to feel pleased about them. If we had not
made love we could have perhaps remained friends, but
the simple fact that we did indicates that our friendship is
over. Now I feel that if her marriage is to have a chance I
will have to back away. I feel very sad and alone. I am long
into my manhood and all my friends have not only been
married for years but have children nearing adulthood.

I am awakened in my chamber by a terrible commotion. It
is late at night, two days after the nuptials of my friend. I
attended the celebration but only briefly and for the sake
of appearances because we are still very much in love.

Standing in my room is a servant, white-faced and trem-
bling. Immediately all sorts on images flash through my
mind: is it Mother? Is it Father? What kind of tragedy can
produce such an affect in him? When he finally speaks I
know that it is serious because he addresses me as Master.

It would appear that when my friend's new husband took her to his bed he was outraged to find that she had been taken by another. He flew into a fury and went directly to the home of my loved one and killed her father with a knife in the heart. The poor man, he was guilty of nothing, he did not even know of our liaison.

I feel myself sit on the bed, the blood draining from my face. I look up into the eyes of my servant, and see they are filled with fear; he is telling the truth. I ask him what has become of her. He informs me that she has been sent away by her family. I ask him to bring her here and then immediately to send word to my family on the mainland. He leaves, glad of something to do.

I remain heavy on my bed without moving for a long time. Her father is dead and I feel responsible. He was a good man and if it were not for my actions he might still be alive. I think of her mother and her sister and how they will manage. It occurs to me that she is probably feeling the same way. I think of her betrothed, who thought only for himself, who did not consider her feelings for one second. Perhaps he and I have more in common than I care to admit. It is not a pleasant thought.

Situations such as this are not unheard of, although sometimes husbands are more understanding and forgiving of the past of their new wives. In such cases nothing more is heard of the matter, but if the situation comes into the open a gift of money is usually enough to appease those who feel offended. But to kill... The man was within his rights though, for it is the custom that the father answers for the sins of the children, especially those of his daughters.

When finally she is brought to me her eyes are red from crying and she is not the woman that I knew, but a broken child. She stands before me saying nothing and suddenly it dawns on me that she may think that I, too, am angry with her and do not want her either. I take her in my arms and immediately she starts to sob, and through her sobs her story comes out. After I left she went and pleaded with her father to be released from the obligation of marriage but he would not hear of it. When he heard that she had affection for another he locked her in her room until the wedding. I feel her fists clench on my chest as she relates this part and her anger eases my conscience a little, but not much. The poor thing, she has been through hell.

It is difficult for me to comfort her through the burden of guilt that I feel but I do the best that I can and when she has calmed down a little I call for a servant to prepare a bath, food and fresh clothes, for she has nothing but that in which she is standing. When she leaves the room I feel a numb relief.

Over the next few days we talk long and deep into the night about what has befallen us. Despite all that has transpired, our love for one another has remained firm and it is this that has helped us through.

In due course my father arrives on the island from the mainland; I can see him now as he slowly walks up the path towards the house with his servant Simon at his side. We go out to meet them not knowing what to expect: his anger or his understanding. I am comforted when he approaches, for he looks me up and down, as if to make sure that I am all right, and then when he turns his attention to Ruth, I see only concern in his eyes. He turns back to me and takes me in his arms. It is a very long time since I have cried into my father's chest.

My tears take me by surprise but are a great relief. Since the killing my attention has almost entirely been absorbed by Ruth and her family. I have tried to be strong for her and I have not allowed space for my own feelings. When finally I step back, he turns to Ruth and touches her shoulder gently, almost a caress. He asks us if we love one another and we each reply that we do. 'Then,' he says, 'good may come of this,' and leads us into the house.

I feel safe. Once my father is washed and refreshed from

his journey we sit outside the house and he listens carefully to each of us in turn as we tell our story. He does not interrupt except to clarify a point here and there and then retires to his room leaving us to talk further to Simon.

The following morning we awake to find my father already gone from his bed. I know that he will have gone inland to find a quiet place in nature. He will not return until he has sought council from the spirits that guide him.

When he does come home, it is nearly evening. He is lighter and more cheerful and gathers us together before the evening repast. He speaks first to me: 'Josephes, my son, if your actions with this woman were driven by desire alone then you must bear some of the responsibility for the events that have befallen you. I know you well and I do not believe that you acted in such a manner. However only you know the truth of this, and you must search your heart and your conscience for that truth. If it is the case that you acted in love, then no blame will fall on your shoulders, for you were acting in accord with that which you have been taught by your father.'

He then turns to Ruth and says, 'My child, you have my deepest condolences and regret at the loss of your father. This tragedy has arisen because you have been caught between two ways. I have raised my children to follow their hearts and marry for love. For this I must bear the responsibility; it is not the way of our society nor is it the way of your family to put these things first. Although there has been a terrible tragedy you must not blame yourself for it. One victim of these events is enough. As for the man to whom you were betrothed, he must answer to God for his actions, but it is my belief that he would have made a jealous and possessive husband. I wish that these events had not taken place but what is done is done and cannot be undone. If your mother and sister will accept our help, we will offer whatever protection and succour that we can to them.'

It is clear to us all that my father's words are just and we sit quietly for some time, considering the gravity of what he has said. In due course it is Simon who breaks the silence, 'Come, let us eat.'

During the course of the evening I can feel my father's eyes on Ruth and myself. Despite the catastrophe that has brought both her and him to this house, I can feel his pleasure in our relationship. None of us who are his children have formed relationships that have not been surrounded by difficult or unusual circumstances, and I know that he blames himself for this. It must be at least some relief for him to see his son have such a chance as this.

Josephes' nuptials.

Tables spread with white linen. On each table is piled food: fruit, roast meats and fish, bread, dates and figs, olives and nuts. We are at Canaan, all about us great preparations are being made, for today is the day we celebrate the nuptials of my wedding to Ruth. The building is large, the guest list is long. Compared to my peers I am being married late in life and have had a great deal of time to make friendships. Since it was announced, this feast has been the talk of Jerusalem. For better or for worse I have a certain reputation and those who are coming are expecting an opulent and lively affair.

I am with my wife, there are many friends and relatives present and it is our day. There is much love and happiness and it feels good that our union is so well received. I suspect that it also may be rather a relief to some. My mother and father are pleased with the match and I feel equal with them. As we stand at the edge of the gathering people come in ones or twos to offer their blessings. There are friends of our family, the families of my father's friends within the Sanhedrin, Yeshua's family, some of his followers, friends from Cyprus, relatives from Arimathea and many others.

Outside the building where we are gathered there is a large raised terrace with a wall around it. On this terrace and spilling back into the building itself the whole company are gathered and hushed. I can hear my father speaking. His voice thin and reedy in the evening air, he is speaking of my marriage to Ruth; it is a quiet and dignified speech at the end of which he offers his blessing. He then turns to Yeshua and asks that he bless the food and wine before the celebrations begin. Yeshua moves from table to table holding his palms downward and speaking a blessing. He has the ability to instil into food a particular vitality, an energy. Perhaps it is the same energy that enables him to heal which he turns to a different purpose. I do not know, but food and wine after he has blessed them taste more wholesome.

It is a long and happy evening.

A moment of bliss.
A tree, an olive tree, green against the blue sky. The trunk is old and gnarled and the olives are ripening. There is laughter and sexuality in the air. Ruth is there, we are alone, she is slim and beautiful and we are chasing each other round the tree. She shrieks as I catch and embrace her. I feel her skin through the cotton of her dress. I can feel her breasts and thighs against me; she wants me and I want her. We fall to the ground and express our affection for one another heartily.

Buying a present for Ruth.
A back street in the City; the ground is hard pressed clay and the narrow street is between two buildings. At the end of the alley is a marketplace which I am walking towards. I push my way past the stall-holders who have crowded the entrance to the alley and into the noise and heat and dust of the market. People are yelling, there are livestock, food, cloth and cooking utensils all for sale in this place. I love the markets and spend hours browsing and looking around. I am here today looking for something special.

It is my wife's birthday soon and I am looking for a gift

for her. I find the man I am looking for – a silversmith who unrolls his cloth and shows me his work. I strike a bargain over a beautiful pin that I am sure she will be pleased with. It is a simple design that she can use as a clasp or as decoration. I secure the pin in my pocket with a feeling of satisfaction and continue my search of the marketplace.

Josephes' disappointment.

A vector, the prow of a boat, a wooden sailing boat, cutting through dark blue sea. I am looking down as if from the mast top. My awareness descends into the boat. There is another there, at the helm, his face brown and salted from the sea air. I ask him where we are going: 'Jerusalem,' he replies. I sit beside him in the stern of the boat, there is a foreboding that hangs over us. We talk a little, but not much and finally find our way into the harbour. It seems to be where the boat belongs, for there is a berth ready. We fold the sails and tie the boat up then walk along the stone pier towards the port buildings.

There is a soldier, a Roman, on duty against a wall in the shade, who looks hot and uncomfortable in his helmet. We walk past with no fear, into the city and into the maze of cool and shady back streets. We are more relaxed here and walk more slowly, stopping to talk to one or two people along the way. Passing through the town we arrive at the family home and find someone has left food for us: olives and bread, with water to drink. We are hungry from the sailing and eat. While we are eating my father arrives and he embraces and kisses me. I feel safer with him here but the feeling of foreboding does not lift.

My father informs me that Yeshua is to depart for India. It is not safe for him to stay in Jerusalem, and his education will be better served from the travel. This has been a probability for some time but not one I have cared to dwell on. A discussion ensues; I want to join my cousin on his travels to India but my father is adamant that he will not allow it.

My place is here with the family and on the estate. I am desperately upset This is just the same as when I had to go to Britain without him. Was that not enough? Why can he not see that my relationship with my cousin is far more important than the family and Cyprus?

It is later the same evening. Yeshua has arrived and listens quietly to my arguments and those of my father. He is silent and I am aware that he will not interfere in what passes between us, it is not his place. I know that ultimately he will accept Father's judgment and it is partly because of this that I do also, although reluctantly. There is some comfort at least in seeing the way that he seems to see and embrace what is inevitable.

Watching the sunrise.
It is shortly before Yeshua's trip to India. I can see his shoulder dimly to my right side. We are in the desert and it is dark and cold. Yeshua points towards the east and there on the horizon is the faintest streak of grey light. We stand motionless, watching intently as the streak spreads gradually across the horizon and the sky begins to lighten with the coming of dawn. We are both captivated by the slow majesty of the spectacle that is unfolding before us and not a word is spoken as the sky brightens from grey to primrose to the lightest azure.

The great sun bursts over the horizon sending shafts of pink and yellow, orange and crimson light into the sky, casting long shadows behind even the smallest pebble. We stand in the golden dawn light, our faces and bodies bathed in the softest caress that the sun can afford. It is so strange that the simplest pleasures are the ones most frequently overlooked, and how many people sleep through the most awesome sight in creation, assuming that light is their right rather than their privilege.

Only when the great disk has torn itself free of the horizon and we can no longer gaze upon it with the naked eye do we turn to each other and start the walk home.

Missing Yeshua.

A memory of loss. I cannot describe the pain of losing him, even for a short while, and now he is gone indefinitely. It is a pain that is so intense, it is physical. A darkness descends that permits no self-appreciation, no contentment or peace; there is only an aching emptiness where once he had been. Every other thing seems grey and pale and meaningless by comparison.

Chapter 6

Cyprus

A tree of some sort, some kind of palm. At its base, whitish sand and rocks and a blue sea. It is hot but the breeze off the sea is gentle and constant. We are sitting on the roof of our Cyprus home. There is a white dome which we are leaning against. When the sun becomes too hot we can sit on the shaded side but at this time we are seated in the sun, on the side that faces Jerusalem. This would indicate that it is morning.

There is a ladder placed against the side of the house and this is the means by which we gain access to the roof. There is no parapet wall and although the building is only one storey high we take great care when there are children present not to allow them too close to the edge. The Cyprus home is built on a peninsula that juts into the sea, wider at the tip than close to the land so it is virtually an island, surrounded on all sides by the sea. The roof is the best place to take advantage of the breeze.

There is a call from below and we make our way down the ladder and into the house. The area we use for eating is open on two sides, a covered courtyard with arches to support the roof. Its floor is surfaced with red clay tiles and it is also on the side of the house that faces Jerusalem. To the left of the courtyard area is a charcoal-fired clay oven which is used for baking bread. In front of this area is a dusty patch of sandy soil that is favoured by the little children who can play there safely whilst being watched over by the adults.

Life in the Cyprus home is intentionally kept simple; a minimum of the beautiful things that adorn the Jerusalem home have been brought here and that which is unpretentious and rustic is rejoiced in. There are so many happy memories of this place: of sitting under these arches talking and laughing into the night; of childhood, playing and swimming in the sea and of growing up in nature and close to the elements.

Josephes settles in Cyprus.

It is nearly two years since the death of my wife's father and I have made Cyprus my home. I often spend the evenings on the high rocks that overlook our home where I watch the sun go down and think through the day. It is always a time of reflection for me when I am here, I think back over my life and about my family and friends. Tonight I am thinking of Yeshua in India. I recall how outspoken he could be, and how often he was misunderstood. In much of the reasoning of the Jews and even of the Essenes there is a certain complacency towards the suffering and unfairness of life. They consider that through such experiences wisdom and understanding will eventually accrue, and I have some sympathy with this view.

Yeshua did not. As a young man he was often very impatient and angry with what he saw around him. He had his own political views, blaming the Romans for much of what had befallen the Holy Land, but this was largely frustration at his feelings of impotence to be able to do anything about it. The ability of man to be unmoved by his fellow man's suffering offended him and hurt him very deeply, but then he did not recognise his own sensitivity and depth. He assumed that all men felt as he did and was often genuinely surprised by their superficiality.

Josephes relaxes with his father.

I am looking at the back of my father who is looking out to sea, his hands on his hips. I approach him and stand beside him. He does not come to Cyprus as often as the rest of the family but when he does he often gazes out to sea. He greets me and I stand beside him for a while looking out to sea, as he does. Suddenly he laughs and asks, 'What do you see, Josephes?' I reply, 'Where the water meets the sky.' 'And what of it?' he asks, 'That must be the place to be,' I reply. He is pleased with my answer and laughs again and, putting his hand on my shoulder, says, 'That is where the heart is.'

There is a rather more forthright side to Father's nature

that is revealed when he is in Cyprus, a hearty and direct attitude to his family. I think it is because of his absence from Jerusalem, his studies, his work at the Temple and business. He is more relaxed, more available as a man and a different kind of father to his sons.

Meditating by the sea-shore.
I am sitting on a cliff top or a hill overlooking the sea. I am alone. I can feel tears cooling my cheeks. I have been crying but now I am beginning to feel more at peace, looking out over the evening sea. It is my favourite time of day, when the rhythm of the day pauses for a moment before the rhythm of the night takes over.

Sometimes I get very depressed; I wonder if it is because my mother suffers in this way, or because I miss my cousin. Sometimes I feel so terribly alone. There is no reason to, I am surrounded by those I love and who love me. At times such as this I seek the solace of the seashore or, when I am on the mainland, the desert. Then a feeling like this takes over, as if I am remembering a stillness and completeness that I lost a long time ago.

The presence of Yeshua.
I am on one of my frequent trips to the mainland. Although Cyprus is my home I return often, when my father is away or to visit family and friends and to conduct business affairs. I have taken some time for contemplation in the desert, away from the family, something I miss greatly when on the island. I am surrounded by desert flowers, the most fragile and beautiful of blooms. It is impossible to imagine how they are able to survive the terrible heat of the day and the freezing cold of the night, but they do. I feel a great empathy with them, alone in the desert, alone with a feeling of sadness and loss. At times like this the vastness, the stillness and the quiet is a great comfort to me, it puts my problems in perspective. It seems an age since Yeshua left for India and I miss his company and friendship more that I imagined I might.

There is talk amongst our friends of a small party making the trip to meet him there. I would dearly like to accompany them but my family depends on me more and more these days. I have not even broached the subject with my father as I know what his response will be, and this is what has given rise to my current melancholia. I am sitting in a place Yeshua and I discovered as children – it was a favourite spot of his, too. As I sit wondering what he is doing now and where he is, I begin to feel strongly his presence beside me. And then it is gone, in an instant, and I dismiss it as a figment of my imagination.

Despite my denial, for several days I cannot shake off the freshness of feeling Yeshua's presence in the desert. It is like the content of a powerful dream that can be returned to again and again without ever losing any of its vividness or vitality. After some time I mention the episode to my father who is preparing for a short trip. He is aware of the plans of my friends and I know he is sensitive to my feelings at this time, but even so his answer surprises me: 'I feel it, too, and I believe that it is not just nostalgia.' I should have realised, for he shares a bond with Yeshua that is equal to any. He goes on to tell me that he thinks that the sensitivity can be developed with practice, and that in this way we can maintain the relationship and its importance to us both without the necessity of travel. He says that by these means Yeshua will still be able to derive the strength he needs from us to go on. He climbs on to his horse and finally says a little mysteriously, 'It shows that time and distance cannot break the bond of love.'

During the course of the weeks and months that follow when I am back in Cyprus I think often of what my father has said. It happens in the quiet moments, when I am alone, then I feel Yeshua close. I imagine that I am feeling what he is feeling, then I argue myself out of it. Sometimes there are images but I tell myself that it is my imagination. It is difficult to distinguish what is generated from my own mind and what is not, but as time passes these incidents of communication become more and more insistent and unmistakable.

I am standing looking out at the sea and in good spirits, thinking about Yeshua, what he is doing and what he is learning, when suddenly I feel his presence again. Perhaps it is that I am now prepared to believe what my father has said that makes it so powerful. It is so tangible that I look round, truly expecting to see him approaching, but I am quite alone. Then I feel his need. It is not demanding, but I can feel his sadness and I can also feel myself start to resist. It is not that I do not want the contact, it is just that all the problems of my daily life and business suddenly clamour for attention, as if they are threatened by this new demand. I try to concentrate my attention on breathing and staying still and then my heart warms and he is there. For a few brief moments the emotional contact is so intense that he may as well be by my side, then gently it recedes and is gone. I am a little stunned, for this, though brief, was unmistakable. It is hard for me to think rationally because it is as if a vast space has opened in my mind, but I know that I will not be able to argue myself out of it this time; the communion is real.

These moments of rapport with my cousin happen more frequently as time passes. They are difficult to describe. To say that he talks to me would not be correct, for talking implies the use of words and there are none. It would be easier to say that he touches, he shares himself, he gives his knowledge and understanding but also his needs, his fears and insufficiencies. There is no separation between them, he comes as a man. But it is not just what he gives that is important, it is what he takes away. His presence, both physical and mental, replaces despair with hope, longing with fulfilment and tears with joy. There is no other cup that tastes so good, that is so inexhaustible, so fulfilling, no being so gentle or so deeply respectful. And still he needs those of us who love him, he needs our understanding and strength as much as he gives it. In a way the lack of his physical presence only serves to make the complex nature of his character more clear and acute.

Nostalgia.
Bright sunlight streaming in through the cracks at the edge of a shuttered window. I am on the island of Cyprus at the farm of a neighbour. This room was used for keeping animals in, but now it is empty save for some dust and debris on the windowsill. I am a man now, with a wife, children and responsibilities and although life on Cyprus has its advantages, I am not immune to occasional bouts of loneliness and when I am lonely I sometimes seek the comfort of nostalgia.

I turn back towards the door which closed behind me, my eyes adjusting to the light. Hanging on the back is an old robe or blanket but that is not what I came here for. This empty outbuilding is full of ghosts, memories of my childhood. When we were little this building was used as a maternity room for animals. Whenever there was a foal or calf or donkey born, it would be here. So many times the children would gather to watch the miracle of birth, then visit each day to watch the progress of the young animal. So much learned in such a small room: of the special soft call that a mother reserves for her young, of the gentleness and innocence of animals and of the trustworthiness of instincts. They are such fond memories.

A loving memory of Josephes.
I am thinking back over my life – I have had plenty of time for this since I came here. In my memories I can see Eli and myself fighting, the kind of bitter fight that young brothers have over nothing. It falls to Rachel to make the peace this time. These are sad memories, of holidays ending and having to return to Jerusalem, of Father being away on business, of Mother being ill. I feel troubled, incomplete.

I think of the times when I would compare myself unfavourably with my cousin, feeling his gifts to be greater than mine. I wanted to accompany him in the discovery of those gifts, but what he would uncover as he grew, I could not. I admired his talent but I also resented it because I felt that it made us different and therefore separated us. We were aware of this, though, and even talked about it; he needed something else from me.

I can see him now in my mind's eye, standing on the shoreline, aged about thirteen or fourteen. He was so simple in his approach to things and when he smiled he radiated happiness. Perhaps the truth is that I do not feel complete without his company, a little like lovers in the early stages of a relationship, I miss him desperately. In my imagination he calls me over and we walk along the shore, the same shore as I am walking along now. There was a looseness about him as he walked. My build is broader and stronger, but he has a lightness and suppleness in his gait, as if his body does not get in the way of his movements. His arms hang naturally by his sides and his fingers are long and delicate; he is upright. He touches the world so gently, almost as if he is not here. Remembering the times we spent together as youngsters changes my mood. The evening is cool and forgiving, the breeze light, a bit like he is. I become quietly aware that his presence has filled my imagery, we talk little, there is no need, but there is an intimacy, a knowing, that all who are in his company experience. It is enough just to walk and to make our way back to the villa.

A visit to the mainland.
I have just returned to the mainland from Cyprus. I visit as regularly as I can and I have made my way directly to the Temple, which I can see in front of me now: a magnificent building made of honey-coloured stone. As I approach it I step into the cool shadow that it casts and start to climb the long stairway that is cut into the stone of the flank wall. It is a long climb; the Temple is a vast building. Having

got to the top I make my way along the parapet wall to the front entrance. There are entrances in the side but I want to go round to the front which is in bright sunlight.

I go in; there is an outer courtyard and that is the part that I am going into. Nobody is allowed further unless on special business. Beyond that there is a special inner temple which only certain people are allowed into. This outer courtyard is where all the business is done and there are rooms built into the walls, with lots of people and different factions represented. My father has a room here and I have come, unannounced, to find him. Not surprisingly, when I find his room he is busy with someone. I settle down to wait with my back comfortably against a pillar and watch all the goings-on in the courtyard.

Family business.
I do not have to wait long. I see my father emerge from his room and look around for me, obviously having been informed of my arrival. We embrace and walk together back to his room, his arm around my shoulder. It is good to see him, it feels as though I have been on Cyprus for some time. In his room there are a couple of low chairs, a couch and a low table, and the walls are hung with tapestries and silks. He sends for refreshments and we sit and talk about the news. He wants to know what is going on in Cyprus and I want to know all about the events in Jerusalem.

The refreshments arrive and I am glad to see that he has arranged some food. He blesses the food and we eat where we are sitting: bread, olives and some kind of cold green vegetables dressed with olive oil. As we eat we share our news, mostly about people, what has happened to this one or that one, problems with the business, how the children of servants and employees are.

Our conversation turns to my brother, Eli. I ask after him but my father has not heard of him for some time. He spends a great deal of time away from the family with the followers of John the Baptist. It troubles my father, who doesn't really like religious politics. I am even more vociferous in my disapproval. I feel that Eliazar has had the benefit of a certain freedom which has been denied me, and I feel angry that he appears not to pull his weight in the family.

My father changes the subject to the business and a long discussion ensues about the plethora of interpersonal relationships that surround our business: who is saying what to whom, who is getting married, who will or won't work with whom, who has had an accident and who is ill and how we can help – all the hundreds of little stories and decisions that make up the work of our household. It is not very dramatic, just life with all its little problems.

Teaching Greek.
We have finished eating and are cleaning ourselves up with little linen towels. We are both reclining in our seats and laughing at some of the stories we are telling. In fact my father is not so much older than me, only twenty years. The conversation comes to an end as he has to teach a class this afternoon and he says that he will see me at home, then pauses, 'Unless you would like to help?' Part of his work is teaching Greek, and he has mentioned several times during our conversation how impressed he is with my Greek since I started living on the island with Ruth who is Greek herself. I agree to stay.

The class is made up of about sixteen or eighteen young men, (there are no women here, only men are allowed in the Temple). Some of them are known to me, being the children of members of the Sanhedrin or of other families that are friends of ours, but nobility is not a prerequisite for learning in my father's classes. There are also young men who are here because he has recognised their talent and their need.

He teaches the class by talking to me in Greek and then explaining to them in Hebrew what has been said. He encourages them to make conversation with me and then helps them with their erudition and grammar. It is quite creative, and I am pleased to be the centre of attention in this way. I have to be quite careful about my pronunciation, though; since I have been married to Ruth I have learned a lot of Greek slang.

As the afternoon wears on I get to know the students better. There are one or two who are quite bright and working hard; others are bored, sent here by their parents, no doubt. When the class ends some of the young men spend a few minutes with my father asking questions, and there is homework to be given out, too. One or two talk to me, asking to be remembered to friends on the island and asking for news.

The Jerusalem home.

The walk home is spent discussing the students in the class: what is going on in their lives and their families' lives and all their trials and tribulations. It seems to me that virtually all our time is spent discussing all the relationships and social interactions of the people we know. He asks my opinion of the students and how they are progressing and we enthusiastically compare and debate their abilities – it is quite humorous at times.

As we walk I see the house come into view at the top of the hill. It is a very grand affair indeed, slightly Moorish architecture, very opulent. It is quite unlike the simplicity of the house on Cyprus. As we approach I see a servant duck inside to inform the household of our arrival. We enter the hall, cool marble with pillars, and a servant takes our outer garments. Immediately my mother arrives; she is so pleased to see me and makes such a fuss! Our relationship is more one of friendship than mother and son and I know she misses me desperately when I am on the island, and I miss her too.

Next the servants arrive; there are a lot of them, and I greet them in turn, especially Simon who is also a close friend. It is an interesting relationship with the servants. On formal occasions such as this one there is a deference,

stopping him occasionally for clarification or to be sure that he has understood. Then he leans back in his chair for a moment and asks a question. He looks away for a moment, thinking, then back at the young man and starts to speak. His explanation is largely a discourse on the Jewish laws pertaining to the problem, but towards the end he pauses to give advice. He then asks if this has met the young man's need. It has. The man offers his thanks, bows and then takes his leave.

My father then turns to me and explains briefly why he approached the problem in the way that he did and the deeper issues that were affecting the situation. Once he has finished this another steps forward for advice and counsel. I am here at my own request, and this method of teaching through apprenticeship is standard for those who wish to learn healing and counselling within the Jewish tradition. What is unusual in my case is that I am not a member of the priesthood, and in this respect my father has bent the rules a little.

Since Yeshua has been in India I have had time to reflect on my own spiritual development. Both Yeshua and my father have commented in the past on my ability as a healer, but despite their recognition and encouragement it is not something that I have ever bothered to develop. The reasons for this are twofold: firstly, as a younger man I was quite rebellious. In my attempts to find my own identity I turned my back on the traditions of my people. Secondly, I compared myself quite unfavourably with my cousin. Whatever gifts were mine seemed insignificant when seen alongside his. I had hoped that my talents would develop in the same way as his but now I have accepted that they will not, and this has freed me to develop them in the way that is mine. I may not be able to do what my cousin can do, but at least I can do something, however small, and it is this that I am here to cultivate.

As he works and talks to the people who have come for his help, my father occasionally turns to me and asks for my opinion. When I am accurate in my perceptions he nods, when I am off-course he says nothing, but when the interview is finished he turns to me and points out a different way of looking at the problem. The work is not all counselling and advice; from time to time he gives a blessing or offers healing by opening his hands over the person's head. Sometimes two people come with a dispute and he listens carefully to each one before giving a judgment that satisfies both. He is very skilled in his work and his knowledge of Jewish law and precedent is enormous, but this is not my main concern. I am here to learn how to help with words and hands.

When we stop for refreshment he questions me in detail on each case we have heard. Although he works strictly within the tradition of our people his approach is different to many of the other rabbis. He has a broad understanding of the spiritual traditions of the Essenes, the Egyptians and of the spiritual practices in India. He has made links between the principles behind these religions and our own, and it is these principles that govern his approach.

In the afternoon several of those who have brought children step forward and in each case, after he has talked with the father, he says, 'My son has talent with children, he will give the blessing.' Then I step forward and give a blessing to the child. He is most insistent that I heal with the blessing, that it is not just words but a conveying of God's grace. He says that anyone can speak a blessing but few realise the true significance of the action, even rabbis. He says that people will accept what they expect, anything too outlandish will cause fear and suspicion. So the healing must be given in the way that they understand. I agree with him on this point and that is why I have chosen to develop my own talent within the way of our people.

Feeding the donkeys.
I have been back in Cyprus for several months. It is late afternoon, the sun is yellow on the calm sea. I am in an outbuilding from which the sea is visible; there are bales of straw in the outbuilding which I am pulling down. I can

see my hands, brown, delicate but strong. Hands that I have now discovered have some healing power. I am dressed as I always dress: a brown robe over a white tunic and red and white patterned silk on my head.

I am on a part of the estate in Cyprus. There are many servants but I still participate in the manual work. I am unbinding straw to make bedding for a newly born donkey and her mother. I have always been particularly fond of donkeys, of their capacity for work and loyalty. My wife comes to see the donkey and brings the children, one in her arms and the other at her feet. It is a peaceful moment; I look up, out of the door of the pen at the setting sun.

Selling timber.

I am with timber buyers who have come to Cyprus to buy beech, for the whole island is forested and our family own the rights to most of it. I am able to negotiate a good deal with them and am also able to arrange shipping using our own fleet. In many parts of the mainland, timber is scarce and there is a demand for good quality lumber. The wood on Cyprus is plentiful and there is a great demand for it. It is a side of the business that I have built up myself. It requires careful husbandry of the resources but many of the islanders have great experience in choosing which trees to cut and I have enlisted their aid and have learned much from them.

The business side of things has not been difficult to learn since much of it depends on the personalities of those involved in the transaction and the relationships that are formed between people. I feel that the ability to make friends of the people I meet is a strength, and as long as all parties feel that they are getting a good deal there is no problem. The only difficulty is those people in business who are greedy or who want to get something for nothing, but their greed makes them weak.

What is giving me more satisfaction now is that my abilities as a healer are becoming known. The islanders have always known of my father's powers and whenever he comes to visit he is sought out for his help. Like him they have also encouraged me to heal since it is known that the gift runs in families, but in the past I have declined. It is ironic that usually the last person to see the obvious is the one who is looking at it. Now it is hard for me to imagine why I did not use my abilities before. I think that it was pride, pure and simple pride.

Josephes acting as head of the family.
I am sitting on the top of a high hill overlooking the peninsula upon which the Cyprus home is built. Ruth is with me and we are awaiting the arrival of a boat from Jerusalem. We see the sails on the horizon and set off down the hill towards the cove where it will berth.

We reach the cove as the boat rounds the peninsula and we are able to see those on board; they wave to us. Amongst others there is Mother, my brother, his wife and children and my sister. When the boat is tied up we help them ashore and then help them carry their personal possessions to the house. On the way we talk of news, of the island and of the mainland. There are some business arrangements, and my mother has brought a letter with some written instructions from my father.

Later in the evening I give some money to my brother. There is tension in the giving; I think he resents being beholden or dependent for his livelihood on the family. It is not easy for him to accept it but he has to in order to survive. I think he also rather resents the fact that his elder brother mediates in these matters. It is easier with my mother, for being the elder son means that there is an expectation that I will perform certain functions. When my father is away I must perform his duties and this is always the way within the Jewish families. Fortunately it is never enough to interfere with the love that prevails within the home for long.

Father arrives.
I am sitting on a shore. I can hear the sounds of children

playing and the happiness that surrounds them. I am with Miriam, my mother, and we are sitting watching the children play in the shallows. We get on well together, there is a familiarity between us that has always been present in our relationship. We talk about everything: of Father who will be arriving soon, of Yeshua, Eli and Rachel, for my mother confides in me as I do in her.

She reaches across, touches my arm and points out to sea where there is a boat. It is Father arriving. We gather the children and make our way to the jetty to meet them. It is a warm meeting. With Father there are others, Yeshua's family from Jerusalem, so there will be a feast tonight. We help them unload – he always brings gifts for the children, who clamour at his feet – and walk together happily chatting to the villa.

A family gathering.
The sparkling blue sea, and tall trees, small fishing boats and some whitewashed houses off to the right. I am looking out to sea. Joseph and Miriam, Eliazar and myself, our wives and children, Mary and her children and many other members of the family are present. All are standing or sitting in groups talking together. There is bread, olives and wine for those who desire it. It is a time of happiness; the younger children are shrieking and laughing, running and playing between the adults.

I am sitting with Mary and Ruth talking about the news of other members of the family and word from Yeshua in India. There is laughter, lightness in the discussion, news is shared of the other families on the island and on the mainland, everyone has an opinion about what is being shared and all opinions are aired thoroughly. It is an easy and happy time. I have a feeling that the meeting is at the time of midsummer solstice.

Josephes supervising the Cyprus estate.
A road or path, through hills. There are others who are travelling in the opposite direction, a man with a laden

donkey, a woman with a child. We smile and exchange pleasantries as we pass one another. I am on my way to visit a part of the island where timber is being cut for shipping to Jerusalem. It is important that only certain trees are taken so as to ensure that the forests are properly maintained and not depleted.

When I arrive at the site I take time to check the work and observe that everything is in order. When I have finished speaking with the people who are working there I move on to the home of one who is in charge of some arable land. He is a native of Cyprus and we talk for some time in Greek about the land and the progress of his work. Later in the day I will make my way to a small coastal port to spend time with those who work there and are responsible for loading and maintenance of some of the vessels that we use.

It is a picture of a typical and routine day of work which consists largely of a tour of the people and businesses that are on various parts of the estate. Many have great respect for my father and so relate to me in a less formal and more friendly way. Sometimes I stop and work with them if extra hands are needed. There are always small problems that arise but I know that the smooth running of the estate depends very much on the kind of contact and communication that those who work here feel that they have with myself and the family.

Mostly I walk when on Cyprus, sometimes with others and sometimes alone. I enjoy walking alone – it gives me a chance to think. Today as I make my way down the rocky paths near the coastline, suddenly I see him standing on a rock, the blue sea behind him, a loose white surplice over him. His head is turned slightly over his right shoulder towards me and he is smiling. He is bearded and tanned, slim, with auburn hair bleached red and golden by the sun. Blue eyes and even, white teeth. His delicate hands are at his sides – I can see the brown turn to white on the edges of his fingers – and in his eyes... such love.

Josephes relates to the spirit world.
I am leaning on my staff looking out over the sea towards the sunset. The sky is streaked with reds and ochres and purples; the sunset has put me in a wistful frame of mind. My thoughts turn to family and friends on the mainland. There is always a regular traffic of people back and forth so there is no shortage of news or company but sometimes I feel rather distant just the same.

Tonight is different, though, for the sunset has put me in touch with a deeper feeling of belonging. It is not a feeling that translates readily into words, it is as if I am remembering something I once knew very well but have forgotten. It is the same feeling that arises when gazing into the embers of a fire: the memory of another life, another reality that runs parallel to this one but is infinitely more satisfying. Another life that can occasionally be glimpsed but never held.

Looking forward to a reunion.
The heat of the sun on my back and shoulders. I am walking down a dusty road alone, wearing a brown toga and white headcloth. I know this road well, it leads to the villa. I round a corner and the road slopes downhill. It is summer, the fields and valleys to either side of the road are scorched brown. In the distance the house comes into view and beyond it the blue sea.

I have been away overnight to a neighbour's house and as I return home I am looking forward with anticipation to meeting family members and friends from the mainland. I know that they have arrived because I can see the mast of the boat in the bay adjacent to the house. As I draw closer I can see one or two in the courtyard to the left of the house and quicken my step. They see me approaching and wave, and one man sets out towards me. He is a close friend of the family who has accompanied my mother for the trip.

I can taste the olive oil on my lips and there is also the

pungent smell of food. There is an earthy taste to the food, the vegetables are grown locally and are very fresh. I am sitting at our table in the open air. My wife, our children, my brother and his wife are here and so are my mother and sister. I am seated at the head of the table which would indicate that our father is still absent. It is a midday meal and we are all enthusiastically eating and talking at the same time.

A servant appears at the table and indicates to me that a visitor has arrived. I stop eating and make my way to the main entrance in the front of the building to welcome them. It is my father with his servant, and they are tired and hungry from the trip. They make short work of shaking off their outer garments and I assist them in washing their feet. Father waves his hand when I turn to call the rest of the family, not wishing to disturb their eating, so when he arrives at the table there are gasps of surprise and welcome. I move my plate and he sits where I have been sitting, a mark of respect that is given and received without comment. His servant sits next to my brother for they are quite fond of one another and they begin talking.

It has been a long journey for them and when Father has eaten and drunk a little he begins to give his attention to the children. It is his way – always he gives his first attention to the grandchildren and secondly to the children. When he turns his attention to us he brings the best news I have heard since I settled here: after ten years Yeshua is coming home!

Itinerant musicians.
I hear music, a drum, some sort of reeded pipe and singing. I am in the marketplace in Jerusalem. I make my way towards the throng that surrounds the players. There is a small troupe that is led by an old man. There is a woman dancing who I take to be his daughter since they share certain similar features. They are wandering musicians and when they have finished playing many give small

coins to the man. I liked the music, they played with great spirit and although I am amongst the last to give a contribution I give generously and talk to the man.

I ask where they are from. He is friendly towards me and explains that they are from the north. We talk awhile and he reveals a gravity and gentleness in his speech. He is an educated and worldly man who laughs easily. He tells me that although he does not normally tour this far south, he is a spiritual man who has never found solace in organised religions and he has been drawn here by news of a teacher who will come. I congratulate him on his sense of timing and explain that there is one such person, shortly to return from India. He thanks me for my time and help and we part company in friendship.

Chapter 7

Yeshua returns

There is a throng that has gathered at our home in Jerusalem to welcome him back; all have come at short notice. I see him enter with my father. Yeshua is so much older than I remember him, slightly stooped and darkly tanned but now with such a radiant beauty. A number of people move forward to greet him but I hang back, not wanting a public display of emotion. He stops and scans the assembled company until his eyes catch mine, then makes directly for me and we embrace. I am so overcome with emotion that I cannot speak. It has been such a long time. He stands back and we look at each other, tears on his cheeks as there are on mine: 'Beloved Josephes, how I missed you.'

The work begins.
It is a quiet moment; most of those who are not within the family have gone home and Yeshua and I are talking. It is the same man who left ten years ago but now everything that was a delight about him is amplified: his gentleness, his ability to bring healing and love, his sense of humour. There is a determination and strength within him that imposes nothing, for it is suffused with calm and peace. To be in his presence is pure delight.

He talks with urgency about his work and his teaching; he must gather his followers, all those who want to learn and teach in their turn. He says that now he understands his path with absolute clarity, and the first step will be to gather those who will follow, then to send word to our cousin John for all who will follow must first be cleansed.

Yeshua teaches in the upper room.
A single-storey house, whitewashed with a domed roof. As I approach the house, there is a smell of smoke and of cooking. I enter the house where four or five are gathered sitting and as I enter they look up at me; they have not met

me before. One of them asks me who I am and what brings me here. I reply that I am Josephes, son of Joseph of Arimathea. The one who has asked me has steady eyes and is self-possessed. I would judge him to be a charismatic man. He asks, his voice now softened somewhat, how they can be of service to me.

I am looking for the one they call Luke. He replies that it is he and introduces the other members of his party to me. He then enquires how he can be of help. I hesitate, he catches my caution and with a wave of his hand indicates that I may speak freely in this company. 'Yeshua seeks your attendance this night.' At the mention of Yeshua's name the other four fall to hushed and urgent whisperings amongst themselves. He offers me food but I decline saying that we have no time for eating as many are already gathered, so he sets about making himself ready to leave.

Yeshua has been talking quietly to many since his return, and from time to time he calls small groups together to teach them. When he does, each must be contacted through trusted intermediaries; on this occasion I am delivering the message myself. I have met most of the followers but still there are some I hardly know. As we walk briskly through the evening streets together, Luke asks me how I come to know the Master and I explain that we are cousins and childhood friends.

He is direct and open in his communications, poised, educated and self-possessed as he explains where he is from, his profession and how he came to meet Yeshua. He tells me that all his life he has struggled to heal the sick and never has he seen such an accomplished healer as my cousin. Finally we reach the inn where the meeting is called and ascend the stairs to the upper room, where about twenty are gathered. We are late and quietly take a seat just inside the entrance.

I watch the faces of those who are gathered to watch and hear the Master speak, their eyes full of love and devotion. No matter how strong, sophisticated or simple they may be, all are levelled by his presence, all find that place inside that is untouched by the vagaries and troubles of life, that mutely remembers the truth.

There is nothing forced in his teaching; it is natural and entirely organic, for that which he gives brings forth life. In him those who witness recognise what they know but hardly dare hope for: that they, too, are of God and that this God is a loving God, capable of tenderness, under-standing and compassion.

Josephes is baptised.

A shimmering sea, misty blue mountains visible on the other side. It is the Sea of Galilee. I am standing with a group of others, mostly men, on the side of a hill. All are wearing light clothing and protection from the sun because it is the middle of summer. Beside me is another of the disciples who is a close friend and there are others dotted about in twos and threes. We are waiting for Yeshua who is with John, on an island a little way from the shore. It is a long wait and we have ascended this hill in order to obtain a better view of them coming. My friend and I fall to talking while we wait, speculating about the future and what Yeshua's return will mean for us.

They have been talking for hours but now we see them approach, walking up the hill, collecting ones and twos as they progress. We walk down with others to meet the party and when we arrive there is quite a crowd gathered around them. Yeshua is saying that he has passed through the waters of life and that we, too, must undergo this initia-tion. It is with mixed feelings that I listen to this. On the one hand I crave that which will bring me closer to my cousin and closer to God, yet I fear the methods used by John so it is not without some trepidation that I step forward to take my turn.

I can feel his hand on my shoulder, around my back and on my left shoulder. I can see my feet and the feet of John, standing at the edge of sparkling water. We are naked, save for a loincloth. We enter the water together and I can feel his hand on my head as I go under. He holds me down for too long and I start to panic, I struggle, he will not let me up... Finally he releases his hold and I burst out of the water gasping for air.

I had been sceptical about this, for John is inclined to extremes, but I am surprised to find myself cleansed and refreshed in a way that cannot be accounted for by the water alone. I turn back to John who is still waist-deep in the water, half-turned towards me watching for my response. I nod to him and he smiles. He is pleased that I have acknowledged him and so am I. It is not that we are rivals, there is strength in both of us, but he is a man of action and I am more a man of duty, and it is hard for each of us to appreciate the value of the other. He comes out of the water and again I feel his arm on my shoulders. It is a tender gesture from such a fierce man and I feel less afraid of him now.

I am looking out over the glittering expanse of Galilee again. It is late afternoon, after the baptism, and there is a feeling of equality amongst us, a brotherhood and also a peace. This event has marked something, made it concrete and certain. There has been a deep recognition of truth, a recognition that for the time being has taken away the doubts that are wont to beset those who are involved.

We stand in a loose circle, some still dripping from their recent immersion, some already dry and clothed again. Not all of the disciplehood are here; I can see perhaps some twenty-five or thirty. John stands on one side, naked but for a loincloth, darkly tanned, sinewy, his body scarred from scourging and life in the desert, his black hair and beard straggled and wild. His presence of being is in stark contrast to the lightness of being that Yeshua exhibits: while John is the epitome of wildness, Yeshua is the epitome of gentleness. Delicate and graceful in frame and gesture and yet speaking with such power and gravity – if ever there was a paradox, Yeshua is it.

He addresses those assembled in a manner and tone that we will grow used to. Using what will become later one of his favourite analogies he compares the baptismal waters to the spirit of the Father. Each one, he says, has been immersed in the waters of life and so will never be the same; we have been reborn into the realm of God. He talks of our gifts and of how no two of us are the same, how each is free to express his gift in whatever way he chooses. He says that now we are more than disciples, we are messengers of God.

The white rocks and hills along the shoreline are yellow in the evening sunlight. I am walking away from the scene thinking about the day's events. While the baptism has brought about a feeling of certainty and affirmation amongst the disciples it has also stirred some very deep feelings. Some have reacted with a proprietorial and protective attitude towards Yeshua, some are jealous of the closeness of others to Yeshua and some simply wish to serve in whatever way they can. What is clear now is that there is a group that has emerged that will have its own momentum and, within that group, opinion is divided about the best way forward. I fear that those with the strongest feelings will hold sway and, as I have often learned, strong feelings are not always the wisest ones.

The disciples are not special, nor are many of them particularly well educated or sophisticated. They are ordinary people and as such they reflect all the hopes and fears of the community around them, the same peccadillos, limitations, sychophancy, loves and pride. Some are shallow in their understanding while others are deep. It is hard for me, too, to share Yeshua with such as some of these yet I know I must. Yeshua says they have been chosen for one quality alone, and that is their capacity for loyalty.

Since his return I am learning more and more of his experiences in India, the great teachers he met and the rites and initiations he underwent. Yeshua is still there, but all that was possible within him before he left is now real.

He has brought with him a wisdom and understanding that is remarkable; he gives hope for the future in a way that no-one I have ever heard speak in my life has done. Such hope, such light, such love, and all in one man. It would be hard to say that this is the happiest time of my life, but it is certainly amongst the happiest times.

Fears for Yeshua's safety.
Everybody in the family who is close to Yeshua has a view about what is best for him. It is not so much that they seek the power of influence as that he invites their interest simply by virtue of who he is. It is hard to describe the strange mixture of intense gentleness and vulnerability allied to extreme depth and understanding in his make-up. He is a paradox – ancient and innocent.

The fact of the matter is that at the end of the day he will do exactly as he has always done, which is no more or less than it suits him to do, but that does not stop those close from trying to influence him. On this particular occasion I am resentful of the pressure I feel that Mary is putting me under, but neither of us fully understands the deeper implications of what is going on, we are just frightened for him. He is only recently returned from India where he had gone in part for his education but also for his safety – just as we had all fled to Egypt to protect him when we were younger – so to have him back in Jerusalem is to have him back in danger, a danger that increases daily as news of his return spreads.

Our discussion is cut short by the entry of Yeshua himself. We both look up and he immediately takes in the situation. He sits beside his mother and covers her forearm with his hand. 'Your work is done and done well, Mother. There are none now who can influence my path but the Father. I am in his hands and it is mine to do his bidding, and yours, too. I can neither be saved nor destroyed until such time as he decrees it, for I am vulnerable only to him. Fear not for your son; he is already saved.'

Yeshua the Christ.
I see him standing. To see the Master Christ emerge from within the man Yeshua is indescribable. Nothing within my life has prepared me for this. He becomes entirely suffused with light; not a light that is similar to the sun but as if it is of another waveform, an energy, a light of majesty and supreme knowing.

There is such a presence in him. To witness it is enough, for all fear vanishes and those who see have their faith and hope irrevocably restored. His touch is as light as the feathers of a dove, his eyes know only understanding, his voice touches my heart like nothing has ever done before and his gentleness is profound. He is the living embodiment of a knowledge that arcs back over eons of time. He sees all, he knows all, and all that which he sees, he sees only with love. He is the Master, nothing more and nothing less. To see him irradiated in such a way is to stand in the presence of a living God, who observes every aspect of his creation, no matter how large or small, no matter how beautiful or ugly, with the same supreme love and understanding.

A meeting with the Christed Yeshua.
Palm trees, tall and slender against the blue sky. The Damascus road. There is traffic – animals, a donkey, camels, an ox-cart – but I am on foot, alone. Alone and happy. I am going to meet Yeshua, and I have chosen to walk because he will be walking also. There are Roman soldiers on the road, too, but I do not fear them. There are eagles wheeling overhead in the sky and as I walk I watch their flight.

In the distance I see the man I have come to meet. He is surrounded by an entourage and he speaks with them as he walks; his teaching and healing have begun in earnest. He sees me and I run to him, we embrace and walk back together the way I have come. He is fit and brown from his travelling and he shares news of his endeavours in exchange for news of the family. Some of the news is sad:

he explains that a mutual friend has died but that he is now in the spirit of love. There are others now coming to meet us; each one he greets as an old friend. Many are known to me, some are not but it is necessary for us to walk separately lest a gathering or band should attract the attention of the military.

A profound discussion.
I feel the heat of the sun on my neck and shoulders, there is a light breeze, a sea breeze. There are palm trees by the sea, a building of some majesty, light-coloured stone with pillars – it is a sea port. There are boats, and one sailing vessel in particular. I make my way down a wooden pier and step into the boat, unsteady at first. The boards are dry from the hot sun. Then come Yeshua and several others also into the boat, and there is excitement and a little fear, although all are experienced sailors. It will not be a very long trip; we are headed for an uninhabited island nearby.

It is not possible to beach the boat at our destination so we have to wade ashore, the water about waist-high. The purpose of the journey is teaching and it is felt by Yeshua that the island has certain properties that are conducive to the discourse. It is not simply a lecture that ensues when we are settled, but a full discussion and argument between those assembled. The ideas are not all accepted readily but meet with resistance in some and are disputed thoroughly. Amongst those present are some of the well-known disciples, simple and beautiful men, but also John who is educated and cultured.

The discussion develops into a more thoughtful debate as the importance of some of the ideas is digested. It is necessary to leave as the evening approaches and the tide begins to turn, so when all have had their fill we return to the boat and thence to the port.

Free will again.
We are very close to one another, shoulder to shoulder in a confined space. I can feel the warmth of the bodies and

smell the sweat. We are barefoot and the stones are cool under our feet. We appear to be moving down a passage of some sort. We enter a stone room and sit or stand on a stone bench that is at the base of the wall surrounding the room. There is no natural light here and the room is lit by an oil lantern suspended from the ceiling.

Yeshua talks quietly. There is difficulty amongst the group, unspoken words that hold people in fear, bitterness, envy, anger. Even Yeshua is powerless against such as this. He must obey the law and the law honours free will. He can speak but he cannot open the minds of those who listen; he can love but he has not the power to open the hearts of those whom he loves; he has vision but he cannot fire the imagination of those who will not see. All that remains for him is to speak quietly.

A teaching.
There is a cistern, the site of many of Yeshua's teachings. The cistern is built against a wall; a lower, semicircular wall retains the water that issues from a pipe set above it. It is possible to sit on the low wall and listen to the trickle of water as we speak. Wells such as this one are always a point of meeting and exchanging news and views.

Yeshua has a little water in the bottom of what appears to be a pewter cup. He is swirling it around the cup and studying it thoughtfully as he does so. Finally he raises the cup to his lips, throws his head back and drinks. As he lowers his head he looks at me and places the cup on the wall between us expectantly. I pick it up and repeat the process he has just demonstrated and replace the cup on the wall where he left it.

He says, 'We have shared this water, and you drank it in the same way as I did.' I am puzzled by what he says and this shows on my face so he continues with a question, 'Had you drunk it any differently would you have felt any less refreshed?' I answer no, 'Then you see, it is not how the water is drunk that is important but that it is drunk, for all must drink and if you look at the variety of vessels and rituals that surround this simple fact, and the attachment of each to their own ways of drinking, you will see how easily the ordinary and life-giving liquid at the centre of the ritual is relegated and lost. So it is with religion. At the centre of every religion, however fancy or plain, is the simplicity of Spirit which none can truly do without.'

I remember him saying this to me years ago and how he used the same example to teach those who were gathered then. It is a point he returns to again and again, in parables, in direct teaching, in any way he can. He never tires of explaining the universality and primacy of Spirit.

The Arimathean speaks of the part played by all who follow Yeshua.
It is the scene of a gathering, people moving in twos and threes towards a dwelling-place, and with them are children. It is a feast day and this is a gathering of the family. It is the custom within the family on days such as this for the senior member to address those who are assembled and today this task falls to my father.

He speaks very candidly for Yeshua has started speaking openly and while – save for my father, his mother and myself – there is no inkling of his ultimate destiny, there is knowledge within the family of his mission and all who are assembled are trusted. He speaks of the family having a responsibility to the teachings that Yeshua is beginning to spread, and that each one of us has been drawn to be part of his work and his life for a purpose.

He speaks of those within the immediate family having the least public role. Few of us, he says, will be remembered for our contribution but that will not make that contribution any less important than that of others. Amongst those who are called are the disciples, those who teach, those who listen and those who care for the man, but none who witness that which he is to embody will remain unchanged and in time that change will become as a beacon for those who follow.

Only one Truth.

Something flat and long, a table, and on it two fists. Yeshua is standing behind the table, leaning forward with his weight on his knuckles. He is angry and speaking very firmly with those who are assembled. He is laying down the law. Simon Peter is there and so are several others. The problem seems to be between two members of the group who don't see eye to eye. Each feels that their version of the truth is more valid than the other. There is controlled anger in Yeshua's voice as he speaks and he points out that each time they fight in this manner they presume themselves to be Gods. He says that there is only one God and they are both part of His truth, He is not part of theirs.

He says that when they cling so tenaciously to their own truth they forget this and presume themselves to be the totality instead of a part of the totality. He says that the arrow of truth cannot penetrate such pride and individualism and that the divine archer seeks the mark of humility.

Simon Peter.

A small house, the outside garlanded with the things of the sea: floats, dried fish-bones and pieces of wood washed white and smooth by the waves. In all this is the great presence of Simon with his thick hands and enormous physical strength and size. He lives simply but well for when fish are scarce his capacity for hard work means that he can do the toil of two men if he so pleases and thus is in great demand as a labourer, but it is fishing, the solitude of the sea, his boats and nets that truly please him.

I am drawn to him. He is also my cousin although not as close as Yeshua and because he is poor and of a different social class there is a natural gulf between us. He is uneducated, unrefined but not without insight, intelligence and considerable wit. He has his own wife and children with whom he is especially patient and although his vocabulary is limited we are able to talk at length about the sea and boats and the best way to navigate or deal with this situation or that. But it is not truly for this information that I seek him out; it is to be beside him. It would be easy to see him in a superficial way, to recognise the strength of body and speech and to walk away feeling that you know the man, but in truth the superficial strength belies a deeper strength, a steadfastness and immovability. Yeshua has aptly named him 'the Rock' because at some very deep level he is still and does not move.

Divided loyalties

I am talking to Mary, Yeshua's mother. We are sitting at a table in the Jerusalem home. She is, as ever, calm, collected and dignified. Since the death of her husband Joseph, she spends more and more time with us. She is speaking to me earnestly and it is a vexed discussion. She wants me to do something which I am very reluctant to accede to even though she is capable of stating her needs and her case very firmly indeed.

Although she commands my respect, she exerts little control over Yeshua who treats her as an equal, a friend and confidante and this we have in common. He relies on each of us in similar ways. There are few he shares the secrets of his heart with and when he does it is sometimes hard for the recipient to bear the anguish alone. Our relationship is one that has contained some of this anguish as well as some very strong feelings, differences of opinion and at times not a little conflict, but there is an abiding love between us, an emotional honesty that is rare even between other members of the family.

This is a most uncomfortable discussion. Mary knows that Yeshua places confidence in my council and on this occasion she wants to find his ear through my words. I feel torn. Much of the difficulty lies in our differing relationships to Yeshua. She is his mother and the love of a mother seeks to conserve, to preserve and err on the side of caution. I am his friend and his cousin and I am more inclined to support his path and mission in life and this is the source of our conflict.

A family meeting.
Yeshua has arrived; he has come alone. Several members of the family are assembled including his mother, my mother, myself and my father. He is tired and takes a seat in a heavy carved oak chair. The two women are already seated, my father remains standing and I am leaning against a table top. The room is one at the front of the house, seldom used and full of dark, heavy furniture and draperies. The windows to the front are shuttered and the light filters in from a window which overlooks the garden at the side of the house.

I know that Yeshua derives great solace from gatherings such as this, where nothing is expected of him. He is here as a nephew, a son and a cousin not as the leader and master. Even when my mother expresses concern about some of his activities she addresses herself to the man she loved also as a boy and not to the overarching divinity that he carries. The earlier conversation between his mother and myself fades into insignificance now he is here. It is no use trying to change his course; all we can do is accept it and offer our help along the way.

Yeshua teaching on the temple steps.
A crowd. Many are gathered. Word has spread far of his powers. On this occasion he is making his way to the Temple steps where he will talk to those who will listen. He is surrounded by a posse of disciples who can be quite firm in protecting him from those who seek his attention. Most of the time I fear that their work is more for their own satisfaction than for Yeshua's protection but on this occasion I feel that their tight formation around him is absolutely necessary.

Within the crowd are those who would gladly see him publicly defeated or, even better, dead. His need for protection is a mixed blessing; he is like a precious jewel, the sight of which would lighten the heart of any who looked upon it and yet it is so valuable it must be locked in the darkness of a vault for fear of it being stolen.

When he reaches his place on the steps he turns to face those who have followed him and indicates to his protectors his desire that they should stand back and give him room to speak.

Much has been made of his capacity to heal and inspire but little has been spoken of the hard daily work of teaching and explaining, the presentation of truths in a way that can be understood, dealing with barracking and heckling and this is largely what he has to contend with today. Those who listen closest, I fear, are those who need no convincing and those who shout will never be convinced.

There is always one, however, who will come forward, who will see the light in Yeshua's eyes and hear the truth in his words. On this occasion a boy and an old man are turned. I watch their furrowed brows and frowns clear with understanding as they listen and I watch as Yeshua subtly acknowledges their dawning recognition.

To speak of him as a teacher implies that he employs some technique but none is ever discernible to me. When he speaks he engages totally with those with whom he is speaking and with that depth of wisdom within himself. In doing so he speaks directly to that corresponding depth in those who listen. Even good teachers tend to fall into the traps laid for them by their students. In so doing they lose the essence of what they are describing. It is like the physician who can name the bones and muscles of the body and how they work – but what has this knowledge got to do with the exhilaration of using those bones and muscles, of running down a hill, almost out of control, towards a loved one?

Yeshua does not teach by describing. He lives essence and he speaks to the essence in others. Moreover he is not without understanding; he knows exactly what he is doing and saying and why. But this knowledge of his actions seems not to come from that conscious everyday part of his being, but from an altogether deeper part of his mind that is pure awareness and understanding.

Living in the 'now'.

I see him standing. He is leaning with his right hand on a table top looking down. His other hand hangs limply by his side; he is depressed, unhappy. I am standing, leaning with my back against a wall, my arms folded. He is speaking in a low voice, staring at the floor but with a distant look in his eyes. His face is drawn and tired. The burden is weighing heavily on him this evening, he wants release from that which he knows will occur. I listen as he questions himself, questions his purpose and his life. He speaks as a man not as a God, a man who must endure, for whom there is no escape.

He talks of me, of my life and family and of how his life might have been different. It is a dark mood and I say what I can to bring solace. It is not my words that bring comfort and peace, though; at times like this it is my companionship that he needs. I say that nothing can change what will be and he must live each day as it comes. After a while his feelings lighten a little and he says with a thin smile, 'Yes, Josephes, there is always today.'

Again, water as an analogy for Spirit.

Sandy-coloured rocks and the bright verdant green of foliage. The sound of the breeze in the leaves. It is a beautiful day early in the year. There is the sound of water trickling and I am sitting on a rock next to a small spring. There are several gathered and amongst them is Yeshua. The Christ is within him and we listen intently to what he has to say.

He is talking of the elements, of how the desert springs to life with only a little water. He gestures to the barren, water-starved plain that surrounds this place and to the verdant luxury that surrounds the spring itself. He explains that the desert does not fight the water or refuse it, nor does it argue as to the use the water should be put, it simply responds in kind, in the way that the Creator intended. He draws the analogy with people and Spirit. Those who simply accept that they are of Spirit flourish and grow but those who argue about what it is and the ends to which it should be put are trying to sit on the throne of God.

His teachings are analogous, very simple and very profound, and all are struck by the depth that is revealed in this simplicity. He says that the place in which we are gathered is blessed because there is no argument between what is given and what is received. It is natural and the beauty of what is growing here attests this relationship. It is only man who thinks he can refuse Spirit, who can turn away from the spring, and because of this it is only man who can return to the source, and in returning become aware of the Father and of His true nature.

An informal discussion.
A blue silk drape, embroidered with silver, partly covering a bench. On the bench is seated Yeshua. We are in the home of my father in Jerusalem. With Yeshua is Simon Peter, a big man, powerful, bearded and yet possessed of great sensitivity and awareness. He sits in a chair to the right of Yeshua and I am half-sitting on a table facing them. There is a discussion going on, punctuated by Simon-Peter's deep laughter.

The discussion is about some of the disciples and Yeshua speaks freely of his concerns. He is worried about the interrelations in the group. Not all see eye to eye and there is often friction between the members, but the discussion is not without humour and a certain amount of teasing over the foibles of those involved. Simon Peter mimics some of the protagonists, and uses this ability to great effect to lighten the proceedings.

A time of reassurance.
We are in a cave, I think, fairly high on the side of a cliff or rock face. There is plenty of room in the cave although it is not more than ten or fifteen feet deep. The view from the cave is panoramic, looking out over the green fields and desert that surround the City. We are in a leper colony

and there is healing going on. Yeshua is holding the head of a man who is before him, saying a prayer or some words softly as he does so. When he has finished the man moves away and another comes in his place. Other members of our party have oils and powders to dress the wounds with. Simon Peter is there and is assisting Yeshua in his work, his attention rather more on Yeshua than on those who are receiving his healing.

When the work is finished Yeshua calls me over and I, too, receive a blessing. One at a time all those who are assisting step forward for the same attention, and last of all Simon Peter stands before him. I have the impression that this last benediction has been carried out at the request of those present rather than at the initiative of Yeshua. We are all very anxious and need reassurance.

A healing.

Something white by my feet – the back of a man, kneeling. I am standing at the edge of a crowd, looking away from the centre. The man is pleading with me, beseeching me. He looks up at me with tears in his eyes but he cannot see me for his eyes are milky; he is blind. He wrings his hands, grips my ankles and pounds the floor with his clenched fists. He wants to know which one is the Messiah, he wants me to take him to Yeshua.

I start to turn towards the centre of the assembly where Yeshua is but it is not necessary for I feel his familiar presence of peace and serenity beside me. He acts quickly and deftly, reaching down and placing his hand on the man's forehead. As he does so the man screws up his eyes and hunches his shoulders. As Yeshua removes his hand, the man opens his eyes. He looks from left to right in disbelief then up at Yeshua open-mouthed. His eyes are not completely clear but it is apparent that his sight is partially returned. Suddenly he throws himself at the feet of Yeshua, thanking him. This display is met with some consternation by Yeshua who helps him to his feet. He will not permit anybody to prostrate themselves or even kneel before him.

Not all of Yeshua's healings are instantaneous, although some are. Frequently it takes time for the healing to have full effect. Yeshua says that if the person has to learn from the sickness then even he cannot help them; if he were to take the affliction away he would be depriving the sufferer of the opportunity to learn.

A profound teaching.
He bends down and takes a cup of water from the well. He drinks then fills the cup again and passes it to me; the water is cool and fresh and issues from a stone pipe set into a wall from whence it splashes into a cistern. When I have drunk he takes the cup and turns to the followers who are assembled and addresses them from the side of the well.

He poses a question, knowing that all who are assembled have observed the ritual of drinking: 'Is it not true that water is life? If bread is the staff of life then water must be life itself.' There is a muttering of agreement.

'And having drunk my fill, I did not go on my way but passed the water to my brother that he, too, might drink. But remember that first I drank, then I passed the cup. So many seek to teach who have not learned, they speak of the kingdom of God without having glimpsed it, and of love having never felt it stir within their hearts. And what can such as these teach, save their opinions and prejudices?

'There is but one teacher and that teacher is the Father, so do not seek to learn from those who do not give thanks to the one teacher, and do not seek to teach unless first you have learned. Give not of your love but His, for you are of Him, and you will be replenished again and again from His inexhaustible supply.'

The fear of God.
I see Yeshua, by the wall of a house, under a tower of some sort. He is talking to someone and I am standing with them. The man he is talking to appears to be terrified. I can see that he wants to turn and run but he is magnetised by Yeshua's words. I recognise the man as one who is often

on the periphery of the teaching groups but this is, to my knowledge, the first time he has bumped into Yeshua and met him face to face. On the surface their conversation is fairly banal: Yeshua enquires about how he is and where he is from. Eventually they exchange goodbyes and the man turns to leave with obvious relief.

As we walk on Yeshua comments on the enormous courage the man demonstrates in overcoming his disbelief and faintheartedness. He says that in one such as this the the soul shines like a star.

A question of doubt.

A long, low white wall and beyond it green fields stretching into the distance. We are on the outskirts of a town. On this side of the wall is a road. Several are assembled there, amongst them Simon Peter, Yeshua and one or two other disciples. There is always a sense of safety when Simon Peter is present, safety and humour. He sits on the wall next to me. We are waiting for others to come and they arrive in ones and twos. There are many followers of the teachings and each of them has influence amongst their families and friends and this is how the word is spread. Some come out of curiosity and they are the ones who will listen and be moved by Yeshua's words. Others come bearing hostility because of fear and they come to prove that his teachings are empty. Some of them, when they hear, cannot resist the truth, but many use what he says to confirm their prejudices and walk away as empty as when they came.

On this occasion Yeshua uses the doubts that people bring as his starting point. He confirms the doubt and the mistrust that people harbour and says that doubt is there to protect hope, for none would have come at all unless they truly had hope. Those assembled question him, testing his authority but he is dexterous of mind and receives the questioning without rebuttal. He has a deep understanding of the wounded spiritual needs that give rise to cynicism and unerringly addresses this need in each who comes forward. It is an extraordinary thing to observe the atmosphere change from doubt to interest and then to conviction. He never leaves without confirming those who have inquired into their own connectedness to the Creator. He steps in to make the connection and then steps out, leaving the connection intact.

The Anointing.
It is the quality of light that is so striking; it is as if the air itself has a radiance, a lucidity, and time is standing still. All the disciples are here, including my father. Yeshua is bare-foot, dressed in a white surplice; he is tall, lithe and deft in his movements. All who are gathered here have no doubt about who he is. He is exactly who he says he is.

We stand before him and, with a dignity that is almost casual, he speaks the words and anoints the forehead of each with a little oil on his middle finger. Nobody speaks save Yeshua. The mixture of humility and nobility, of depth and lightness seem altogether natural, familiar and yet from another dimension entirely.

Yeshua's great presence.
It is a family gathering, a festival of some sort, and all are gathered for a meal. I am seated next to my cousin. I watch him as he talks: full lips, high cheekbones, hawkish nose, curly brown hair, light cropped beard. His features like his hands are delicate and strong. I watch his mouth intently, enraptured by his speech, the shapes his lips make as he forms the words, the beauty of his intonation and timing. It is as if a beautiful silver light issues from his mouth as he speaks. The language he uses is light and easy yet carries an authority, a beauty and simplicity that none in the room can escape.

The Christ Light.
Someone pulls at his arm and he gestures them away, to stand further away from him. Now he raises his hand to indicate that they have stepped far enough back. He points

to the space between himself and the other man. 'This space,' he says, 'is the way home. Not one single person in creation can enter it with anything other than themselves. There are no fellow travellers and the way will not allow the carrying of possessions; you enter it alone and you walk it alone. There is but one who will accompany you and I am that one. It is I who will walk by your side until you no longer have need of me, but it will not be the love of my physical presence that will draw me to you in your times of need; it will be your love of my light.'

A matter of faith.
I see him standing quite clearly, his right hand raised, the first and middle fingers loosely extended. He is addressing a small group of one or two who, like many others, have heard that he is the son of God and have come to test him, although as far as I know he has never openly made this claim himself. He seeks no retribution nor does he tire of addressing the endless stream of questions, many of which are designed to test, humiliate or prove him wrong. He has an eye and an ear for whether there is a genuine desire to know behind the questioning and to such as these he shows extra patience.

'If it is proof that you seek then you will satisfy yourselves only with that which can be proved and all that which is a matter of faith will be ignored. If you cannot accept your very life and the life all around you as evidence of the Creator you must indeed be suspicious of everything, but if you can then you will also see that we are all His children.

'Open your minds and your hearts to a different kind of proof: to the wind as it stirs the leaves in the trees – is it not applause for the Creator's work that you hear? The warm rain that softens the hard desert, are those drops not the tears of a Creator who cries for the barrenness of His desert? And the birds that soar in the sky, do you think that they do not know that it is the very breath of the Creator that buoys them aloft?

'In truth the proof is all around you. What you are really asking of me is that I quell your suspicions and that I allay your fears. If I were to perform some feat of magic, would you believe it? Or would you seek to peer up my sleeve to see how I produced such an effect? Truly it is doubt that causes you to ask such questions of me, a doubt that ultimately can only be assuaged by faith.'

Josephes happy with his life.
I am in Cyprus lifting my eldest son from the branch of a tree next to our home. He is about four or five years old and laughing. I carry him to the house where Ruth is sitting with our daughter. She is pregnant with our third child. So much has changed for us since our first child was born. Not only because of the happiness that our little family has brought to us but because now Yeshua is part of it again. So much of my time is divided now, constantly travelling from Jerusalem and back to Cyprus.

Come, walk with me.
The city of Jerusalem. There is a house, whitewashed and with a domed roof, which I approach. I knock on the door and it is opened by a bearded, smiling man who recognises me and welcomes me inside. There are about six or seven gathered here, all Jewish, all men. I have been invited here this night by the one who opened the door to talk to them about the teachings but already I am beginning to regret coming, for clearly some have been drinking. There is great curiosity amongst them but I do not know some of them and by their mannerisms I do not find that I can readily trust them either.

In retrospect I know that I should have gone home at this point but I am convinced that I can reach them; after all have I not seen my cousin enlighten even the surliest of his detractors so many times before? As I start to talk they encourage me and seek to ingratiate themselves with flattery but, as soon as I respond, they mock what I have to say, constantly making gross comments amongst themselves and laughing at their own jokes. They are not so much filled with malice as with a prurient obsession with scandal and gossip, blind to the deeper truths that I am trying to impart.

Now I am really wishing that I hadn't come, blaming myself for my arrogance in thinking that I could inspire anyone and wishing that Yeshua were here for he would know exactly how to handle the situation. These men seem to be ruled by a desire to belong to each other, the prospect of not being one of the group seems so threatening to them that whenever one of them says or does anything that is different to the others it is sarcastically ridiculed and derided. Inevitably the discussion precipitates to the lowest level and any attempt to raise the tone meets with further contempt.

As soon as I can I make my excuses and leave but it is with a deep feeling of defeat and humiliation. I close the door on their guffaws and start for home. It is a long walk so I have plenty of time to reflect on my hopes and my failings. I am certain that the only thing these men have gained from me is the means by which they can entrench themselves in their scepticism. To them I have been living proof that the teachings I hold so dear are nothing more than worthless babble. There would be plenty of reason for me to be angry with their stupidity but on this occasion it is not they who suffer the full force of my rage and disappointment but myself. It is not the first time I have had cause to compare myself unfavourably with my cousin and tonight I am more than usually cruel in my analysis of my behaviour and my gifts.

Such is the depth of my despair that, as I walk, I seek the privacy of the shadows and the alleyways, hardly knowing where I am going until I come to a full stop. I sit in a dark corner between two buildings and bury my face in my hands. If I could die now it would be of no matter; not only have I been foolish but – what is worse – I have been seen to be a fool. The darkness of the misery and self-pity I feel is unbearable and it is not long before my eyes are stinging with tears. It is only then that I feel the gentle pressure of his hand on my back. I look up and beside me is Yeshua, but this is no man who is beside me; it is a vision, part light, part presence, and in his eyes the purest love that is possible, and I hear him say softly but clearly, 'Do not cry, Josephes. Walk with me but not for me.'

A question of adaptability and humility.
Low hills are visible on the other side of a barren, feature-less plain or desert. There is a heat haze rising from the plain and we are standing on high ground overlooking this terrain. Yeshua says that from time to time life can appear like this desert: barren, empty, something that holds no promise in itself save that it must be crossed to reach the cool and fertile hills on the other side.

He says that while the plain may appear this way, those who cared to go and examine it would find that it was not barren at all but teeming with life. It is not the life of trees and crops – such grand gestures of the Creator's work are not the province of the desert – but humbler forms of life, cleverly adapted to their environment, live in multitudes in such places. He says that man can learn much from cross-ing the desert. Those that survive the unbearable heat of the day and the intolerable cold of the night do so because of their adaptability, humility and ability to conserve. One of the great lessons of the desert is attention to detail, for in the desert life dwells in the small, the insignificant and the detail.

Obeying Universal Law.
I see Yeshua; he is holding a leaf, still attached to the tree, the stem passing between his index and middle finger so that the surface of the leaf is flat upon his open hand. He is looking over at me, pleased with himself and grinning as if he has just thought of something very important. He says, 'Thousands of leaves on each tree, each one different and each one unique, each one connected to the same trunk and each trunk sharing the same soil and the same

sun. No leaf tries to subjugate another, no tree fights
another, they all obey the Creator. One day man will be as
the leaves on the trees but far, far more beautiful.' And
then he laughs.

Destiny and free will.
A door, green I think, set back in the shade of thick sand-
coloured walls. The door opens directly on to steps which
lead upward. It is a simple room and many are gathered
here, perhaps fifteen men and several women. I am here
with my father, Joseph, who is respected greatly among the
company. There are bench seats and a table; the women
bring refreshments. In due course the excited talk between
those assembled stops and all turn to Yeshua. All are completely attentive to the man they love so deeply and all
observe the miraculous transformation that he undergoes
as he begins to speak: his face lightens and he speaks with
measure and gravity.

He talks of the destiny of man and of how that destiny
will be fulfilled in the reunion with God. He says that
destiny itself has not the power to change things, only man
has that power, so man may seek his destiny and follow it
or ignore it and turn away from it; the choice is his and this
choice is a gift from the Creator. He explains that if man
ignores his destiny and puts only his own needs first then
over time the culmination of this denial will turn on man
and cause his destruction. This will not be a retribution
from God, for God is not capable of such an act, it will be
a consequence of ignoring the laws that govern creation,
laws that are deep in the soul of every man. He likens the
man who turns away from his destiny to a shepherd who
kills the pregnant sheep for the sake of a meal today and
the man who follows his destiny to the shepherd who
follows the laws of nature, reveres life and takes only what
he needs to survive.

A meditation.
I am lying back, feeling the warmth of the sun on my face.

I am alone, and I can feel tears in my eyes and on my cheeks. Nobody knows of my grief, of the welling of emotion, and I wish none to know. So much of my life is spent with people, there is little privacy, so that which I do find is precious to me. A moment's peace, here on the hill overlooking the sea.

Good husbandry.

He walks to a cistern, takes a drink, just enough to moisten his lips on the palm of his hand and then sits on a low stone parapet wall. Several children run up to him; they know that this time is for them. Amongst them are many who are related to him, his nephews and nieces.

He shows them his fist, closed, and asks them if they know what is in there, like a conjurer. The children are delighted and guess what he might have. Finally one guesses correctly, he opens his hand and it is full of almonds. The children take one each and eat them. There is the exact number with one left over, which Yeshua takes himself. He pauses and one little girl asks if he is going to eat the almond but instead of answering he passes the question back and asks, 'Shall I eat it or plant it?' The children are divided on this point; some say he should eat it and others say that he should plant it. He asks the little girl who guessed correctly what he had in his hand. 'Plant it,' she replies. He hands the almond to her and she turns to find a spot in the garden.

She turns back to Yeshua and asks, 'Will it grow?' 'If you water it,' he replies, and goes on to say, 'If we plant one for each handful we eat, and if only one of each hundred we plant grows into a tree, there will always be plenty.'

Communing with light.

I can feel cold air on my face, and the coarse material of a heavy cloak about my shoulders. It is night-time and I am in the desert. The ground is fairly flat with a little scrub and loose rocks strewn about. It is lit by a full moon.

There is someone else in the distance approaching me. It is Yeshua, who has been in the desert for some days, and we have agreed to meet at this place. Far behind me is the light and warmth of the city. As he approaches I can see that he is smiling, smiling and happy. He is often like this when he returns from a fast such as this; he comes back filled with gentle easy energy.

As I wait for him to draw near I think back to how he was before he left. His knowledge was torturing him, each one of his gifts weighed on him like a sharp-edged rock and he longed to be as the other men around him. Now he is renewed and lit from within. He reaches me and we embrace briefly before starting the walk back to town and I am struck by the warmth and tenderness of his touch. We walk in silence and without haste. No words have passed between us, the company is enough.

I know that when he goes into the desert he is graced as no other man is graced. I believe that he communes with the Creator Himself and although he seldom discusses it he does talk of the revelations of angels. From my understanding of what he has shared he does not experience such revelations in the form of words or texts but as light, a light full of meaning that only translates into concepts and words later.

It is this light that he is filled with now, the same light that fills me as I share his company. It is altogether a more elegant form of communication than words. It is an understanding that glides on the wings of love.

Jealous of Simon Peter.

I am looking out over a sea or a great lake; it is the Sea of Galilee. I am standing looking across the water, feeling the refreshing inland breeze on my face. We walk to the water's edge and bathe our feet in the shallows. There are gulls, flying quite low, noisily and close to us, arguing about the spoils created by some fishermen who are working a short distance away. We are making our way towards them.

We have come to see Simon Peter. There is a deep attraction between Simon Peter and Yeshua, although they are as different as chalk and cheese. Simon is big, uneducated, coarse in language and gesture whereas Yeshua is slim, refined, thoughtful and gentle. We are all three related, being cousins, though Simon Peter is older than us. To be honest, the relationship between Simon and Yeshua pains me; of each one alone I am both respectful and admiring but the strength of the feeling between them is hard for me to see. As the disciples have developed and learned, Yeshua has started to confide more and more in Simon Peter. When I am not available, which is often, Yeshua turns to him.

Envy is a hard emotion to feel, much less admit to, but I am powerless to prevent it. I have accompanied him this far, why now should he turn to another? And yet I know, too, that there is a deeper purpose to his actions and that time runs short.

A good catch.
A hand holding a fish, a small fish, about seven inches long, and the gunwale of a boat. The boat is full of fish and there are more tumbling out of nets into the boat. It is Simon Peter's boat and it is with other boats. The harvest of fish is great and those who are on board have their work cut out hauling them in.

A light shining in the darkness.
I am one of a large crowd of people, both men and women, who are waiting. He comes with two or three disciples. The crowd gives way before him and forms a horseshoe shape around him so that more can see and there is a space before him. This is a gathering that consists of many of the greater discipleship who number seventy or more.

He speaks of the Father, the one Creator, and as he does the sky darkens. It is an eerie brownish light which envelops the proceedings and many mutter and shift uneasily. As Yeshua speaks, some begin to look up and point. There is a light in the sky, unlike sunlight, for it is whiter and purer. It is quite clear and quite strong, directly above us. There are gasps and some throw themselves on the ground, hiding their eyes, as slowly the light spreads and overcomes the darkness. As it does, I hear Yeshua saying that what we have seen is but a tiny representation of what will happen when all accept the one Father.

Seeing the light through the veils of the past.

I see a man, slight in build, wearing a light oatmeal-coloured toga; I have a feeling that it is John. He is fair in complexion but with jet black hair and beard. He has brown eyes and his features are fairly sharp and pointed. He has a quick mind but tends to criticism easily; always he changes the meaning of that which he is told or taught to his own satisfaction, accepting nothing without first analysing it. He is a man of the mind, primarily, who tends to approach things head-first rather than heart-first.

John is an educated man, from a refined family background, who can speak several languages and I have this in common with him. There is an interesting relationship between those who are related to Yeshua by blood and are also disciples and those who are not. In many ways the disciples are all united by a common bond but there is a familiarity between those who are cousins or brothers which sometimes inspires the envy of those who are not. In a similar way there is the jealousy of those who are of the twelve from those who are not.

There is a great deal of feeling within the entire group of followers, both positive and negative, as each one struggles with the call to serve in different ways. All are human, all see the light through the veils of their past.

A happy family gathering.

It is a family gathering. I am lighting the candles on the menorah. The men are seated and the women are standing at the sides of the room. There are many present, perhaps twenty or twenty-five. All are family members though the two core families are of Joseph and Joseph of Arimathea. There is a small gift for each one present, and this is something that I have organised. It is Father's place to officiate with the prayers before the meal begins and he does this with dignity and solemnity. It is a happy time, a time of love and sharing, each generation of the family having those of their own age group to talk and share news with.

Yeshua foresees his death.

A memory within a memory. I can see a gaggle of people gathered on the shores of Galilee. I feel very grief-stricken. I am remembering the work of John the Baptist. It is after his death and I am recalling the way he baptised me after Yeshua's return from India. There are many of us gathered here to mourn his passing. We talk of it being a terrible but fitting death – he died as he lived, in a most dramatic and singular manner.

There is great sadness at his loss, for John's work has been seen by many in a different light since Yeshua's return. At some point in the proceedings Yeshua and I walk away from the crowd. I know what he is feeling even though no words pass between us. I recognise in the heaviness of his feelings the knowledge that one day he may suffer a similar fate.

Yeshua's greeting.

Someone is pouring water from a large pitcher into a small bowl which I am holding. Each time I drink, the smaller bowl is refilled until I have drunk enough. When I have finished I look up at the person who is holding the pitcher – it is Yeshua. I have walked a great distance to be here and I am tired and dirty from the journey so the attention that he is giving me is very welcome.

He fills another bowl from the pitcher and pushes it towards me for me to wash my hands and face. He hands me a cloth and when I have dried my face, he says, 'And now you are here! How many times did I pour water for you, cousin?' 'Once for my feet, once to drink and once to wash my face – three times,' I reply. 'Then three times have you been anointed by the Lord: once on your feet that you may walk in truth; once on your face and hands that you may see clearly and touch with peace those things around you, and once for your thirst so that you will always know your heart.' He waits for my response, head to one side, his eyes twinkling mischievously, and so obviously pleased with what he has said that we both burst into laughter at his curious and ironic form of greeting.

Yeshua receives a golden present.

A deep mustard yellow; it is the blossom of a certain kind of flower, a bundle of which is being carried in a basket on the arm of a woman. The flowers are quite common and grow by the roadside in the form of weeds where they dry in the sun. The woman is in some ways like the flowers she carries, old and brittle and poor. She walks very slowly. When she reaches me I offer to carry her basket but she declines and takes my arm instead. We make our way together to the place where Yeshua is waiting.

As we approach I can see him through the door, standing at a table which is set against a wall; in the wall is a window through which he is looking. As he hears us approach he looks round and welcomes us in. He is particularly attentive to the old woman. She goes about her business in the manner of the very old, deliberately and at her own pace. She sets her basket on the table, and Yeshua and I step back and watch as she arranges the plants that she has brought, displaying them to their best advantage. She turns to Yeshua when she has finished with a slightly grave expression on her face and gestures towards the plants, indicating that she has brought them for him.

Yeshua thanks her with respect and humility and listens attentively as she speaks. It is her son, he is a scoundrel and keeps the company of the worst people, he does not look after her and has squandered his father's legacy on wine and women. Now she is poor, she has nothing to offer Yeshua but the plants from the side of the road, but it is not money she has come to ask for, she explains, it is peace of mind. She fears that she is not long for this world and that if only her son would show some sign of settling down she could die happily.

When she has finished speaking Yeshua addresses her, 'Mother, fear not for your son, you cannot learn the lessons of life for him nor can you prevent him from learning his own. He is your son and you have given him all that is in your power to give. Now you say that you have nothing and yet have you not brought me gold this day?'

He gestures toward the dried flowers on the table and with a supreme tenderness he says, 'There is yet gold in your own heart, mother, and when you recognise that gold you will see the gold in the heart of your son. Now go in peace.'

We are outside on the hot, dusty road where I met the old woman. We are looking out over the hills and valleys. We turn and walk slowly down the hill. He is explaining something to me, something about the old woman and the flowers. He says that it is Spirit that heals, not man. All that a healer can do is to direct Spirit but no healer can direct Spirit against its natural direction and this is fortunate because the natural direction of Spirit is to make whole. He says that very largely mankind brings suffering upon themselves by denying this desire in Spirit to make whole.

Yeshua is love.
There has been a terrible setback. Exactly what it has been I cannot discern in this memory, perhaps it does not matter. I can see Yeshua clearly, hands limp by his sides, head bowed forward slightly, looking at the floor. He is gentle in defeat, his capacity for acceptance is awesome. On this occasion no anger arises in him nor yet any blame or recrimination, he simply becomes transparent, and it is clear that it is the light within him alone that keeps him standing. His body offers no resistance to the supreme gentleness of Spirit that glows in his heart. At times such

as this he does not teach love, nor does he preach of love, he is love.

A lame man is healed.

Another teaching situation. I am looking over the heads of a crowd of about eighteen or twenty people. All are wearing headgear against the strong heat of the sun so the scene that presents itself from my vantage point is very colourful. We are descending a slight incline and going down into the crowd. None of us stand out since like the crowd we, too, are wearing head scarves which we have pulled around our faces so that we are able to move freely, without drawing attention to our identities.

We make our way through the crowd; most of them are strangers but one or two I have seen before. Amongst them are women and younger men and one man who is lame, propped up on one elbow on the ground. It is not unusual that at gatherings where Yeshua is due to speak those who have lost hope or who suffer from incurable illnesses arrive or are brought by their distressed families – they have nothing to lose. I and the other members of our party stop at the front of the crowd while Yeshua walks a few paces further on. He turns to face the assembled and, as he does, draws the headcloth from his face, 'It's Him,' someone points. 'The Nazarene.'

There is an urgent whisper that passes through the crowd and I can feel the pressure at my back as they surge forward, craning their necks to catch a glimpse of him. Yeshua acknowledges their curiosity and speaks their unspoken disappointment, 'You came to see the son of God and yet here before you is a man.' There is a silence.

'Then how should we know you?' shouts one person. 'You will know me by my actions and deeds, not by my appearance,' responds Yeshua. 'Then show us what you can do,' yells someone else, taunting. Again Yeshua comes back, 'Your faith will open your eyes, brother.'

As he speaks there is a commotion at the centre of the crowd and shouts and exclamations. All turn from Yeshua towards the source of the commotion and there standing up amongst them, with a look of deep gravity on his face, is the man who was lame and unable to walk. 'It is a trick,' cries one, 'they brought him with them.' 'No,' says another. He says his name and the name of his father and his village and then, 'He is my brother and has been unable to walk since he was a child. He is the Messiah, it is a miracle!' The crowd turns back toward Yeshua but he has slipped quietly away.

Cousin and Teacher.
It is a hard and stark day for me. Given the material circumstances of my life, many would find such a statement difficult to believe. To have definite knowledge that there is a source of love, the purity of which is unsurpassed, would be enough for most people. To meet the person who is possessed of such a love would be almost unimaginable. To know one such as this as a companion and the closest of friends would be an undreamed-of privilege. And yet being in such a position is it not the most curious perversity that I have the stubborn capacity to harden my heart to him?

What strange motive would drive the starving man to dash the food from the hand that offers it? Or the parched to tip the water that is proffered on to the desert floor? And yet on this day I am one such as these. Is it pride? Or is it fear that makes me turn my back on my cousin? I think a little of both, but perhaps mostly it is fear, for so great is my love for this man that I fear that I will lose myself entirely in him. However much I may desire such a loss I cannot help but rebel against it at the same time. Is this not the fate and the fear of all who love? The very thing we crave is that which is most threatening. So I turn from the light, as if it were never there, leaving him to watch and wait until my heart softens again.

I can see him now standing amongst a group of disciples. Cousin and Christ. In such presence there is none of the difficulty that sometimes characterises this group. There is no need for rivalry, no need to stand out, to compete or to demand, no need to be first or last or to wish ill upon those who seem to be closer to the centre than others, for are not all these things at the end of the day attempts to gain blessings of one sort or another? But when one is blessed, when there is the tangible feeling of being loved despite anything that may cross the mind, despite any feeling however negative, any behaviour however spiteful, despite any loathing for self or other, then don't these things lose their power and evaporate?

When Yeshua speaks he speaks with enormous power, the power of truth, and if this power were not tempered with an equal weight of love, understanding and compassion I feel that many of those who listen would be destroyed or driven to insanity by what they hear. It is all very well to seek the truth but the light of truth is so intense that it illuminates not only the fine qualities but every imperfection, the dark corners where a lifetime's failures, humiliations and compromises have been swept out of sight, and who has the strength to face everything that they have hidden from themselves? Fortunate then that it is in Yeshua's nature not just to see with absolute clarity but also to love with absolute dedication that which he sees.

There is such a terrible pain in the love of the Master. How is it that something so simple and pure can be so difficult to accept? It is like a child gazing into a fire, mesmerised by the warmth, the light and the life, and yet the natural desire to reach out and touch the glowing embers, to pass a hand through the flames causes a recoil of pain and confusion. So it is with Yeshua – looking into his eyes is like trying to look into the sun itself. There is only one way to touch such a fire and that is to be the same, to burn with the same intensity of love, knowing that in the burning all will be reduced to ashes. And is this not what God wants? For when all is rendered to ash, is it not love that remains?

A dramatic healing.

A beautiful tree-filled valley and I am walking down into it. There is a river at the bottom and much of the surrounding land has been cultivated to take advantage of the natural irrigation. There are olive groves, fig trees and vines. As I approach the river I see a woman squatting at a large bowl, washing something. As I draw closer she looks up and half-smiles as if she is expecting me and says, 'They are up there,' nodding up the riverbank. I follow the direction of her nod and make my way along the bank path heading upstream. It is a pleasant walk and I can hear the trickling of water from the river as I go.

The path leads into dense foliage and although the way is well trodden the leaves encroach on the path here and there. After some way I hear the voices of people and see a cluster gathered around the entrance to a small one-roomed dwelling. As I approach the door I see Yeshua looking over his shoulder towards me, and he motions me through the spectators and inside. He greets me and the two others who are with him nod towards me with grave expressions on their faces. As they look away I follow their gazes down to the floor where there is a low bed.

On the bed is the sickest person I think that I have ever seen in my life. It is not even clear to me if this is a man or a woman; the face is grey, leathery and dry and the sunken eyes are thick and without light. What is more sinister though, is that this body emanates a chill and a malignancy that is indescribably repulsive. If it were not for the presence of my friends I would flee immediately. I look over to Yeshua to try to gauge how I should respond to the situation but his eyes are on the near-corpse with an unswerving attention.

He motions us closer to him and I feel a tension in my body that slowly increases in the region of my solar plexus. Suddenly the tension snaps and the body on the bed breathes out sharply and convulses as if punched in the stomach. I do not know what shade possessed this poor soul or anything of what passed between it and Yeshua but before my very eyes I see the grip it held loosen as the chill slips away from the body like water from a vessel. I watch with amazement as the light and colour returns to the flesh, the breathing becomes deeper and the body becomes recognisable as that of a young girl, barely a woman. From the door I hear the voice of one of the spectators, 'It is a miracle, she is saved!' And from Yeshua, 'Be in peace.'

Yeshua heals a Roman.
The profile of a man's face. He is lying down. His face is emaciated from disease but still possesses nobility: high cheekbones, a long aquiline nose and a high brow. He is on a bed or couch and standing over him is Yeshua. Behind Yeshua are several others. I am beside the bed. This man is not a Jew but a Roman. His straight black hair is cut in the style preferred by those who hold high office in the military. He is known as a fair man who treats his servants well and it is the servants who have summoned Yeshua to their master as a last resort.

The healing is without fuss or ritual. Such is Yeshua's alignment with the laws of creation that he does not stand apart from them, they are of him and he is of them. That which he wishes is that which creation desires. As Yeshua turns to leave it is apparent that he has not just saved a life but he has changed a life, and indirectly the lives of all who knew and loved this man, for all have witnessed the Spirit move within him.

Josephes witnesses a punishment.
I can see a face, contorted with pain and fear. It is the face of a man who is being flogged, covered in sweat, blood and tears.

Usually I try to avoid the execution ground but on this day I must walk past it. Despite the fact that I had vowed to myself that I would not look up I have been unable to prevent my curiosity causing me to glimpse, to find the eyes of this unfortunate man, and to see in them a chilling equality before they are closed again by the bite of the lash.

Punishments in Jerusalem are severe; scourging, crucifixion and stoning are commonplace. Although the laws are in the hands of the Jewish authorities they are overseen by the occupying forces. Because of this, miscreants are treated firmly and swiftly. The authorities must be strict for if they are not, the Romans will step in; or, as sometimes happens, the implementation of the law is left to those who saw the misdemeanour or who bear a grudge against the accused, in which case justice is dispensed summarily and brutally.

In this city the respect that the Jewish leaders are able to command is based on their ability to maintain order by demonstrating to all that they can take care of their own. There is little room for compassion once a misdemeanour has reached the public forum. I hurry on knowing that if fate had decreed it, it could just as well be me tied to that crude cross.

Remembering John the Baptist.
Witnessing the beating has put me in a sombre mood. As I walk on I imagine the head of John the Baptist, held aloft by the hair, as dull and lifeless as carrion. I did not see it but I have heard that this was the fate of our cousin, and in his fate is a grisly reminder that nothing is permanent, especially that which is so dedicated to purpose. But Yeshua knew it would happen, he predicted years ago that he would not be the first or anything like the last to sacrifice his life for that which he taught. He said that it would show that brutality and murder were not limited to the ordinary but were just as much the province of the educated, that man's capacity to submit to the dictates of greed, lust and seduction is not a matter of refinement or poverty, of wealth or power but is a consequence of living life with the back turned to the light of Spirit.

A parable.
He has a stone in his left hand, about the size of a

chicken's egg and he strikes it with a similar stone in his right hand; they click together sharply. He says that one stone will not break the other because they are of equal strength. He presses them together and says neither will one stone merge with the other because they are too hard; the stone must obey its nature, and its nature is to remain constant. This is why the stone cannot grow, it knows nothing of conflict and love and so it remains the same or gets smaller with the passage of time but it does not grow.

It is not so with man. It is in his nature to fight and to love and through this he grows. He looks upon his works and unless he is akin to the stone, what he sees softens his heart. The stone knows nothing of compassion and there are many who are as stones, but the man who learns from his mistakes is a delight in the eyes of God.

The spirit that animates.

He stands, his weight on one leg, arms folded, his lips pressed together, leaning back slightly. He is looking down at the toes of his free leg with which he is tracing a pattern in the sand at his feet. His eyes have a faraway look; he is waiting and contemplating. He speaks without raising his head and speaks to no-one in particular: 'This earth is no different from the body of he who speaks with you, they are the same. It is the spirit that animates each that is different. There is no one thing in creation that is more or less of God, no icon, no image, no plant, animal or person, only the spirit within.'

Yeshua's doubt.

He is standing at one end of the table, leaning forward slightly, with hands raised, palms uppermost. He is appealing to me and questioning, 'How can they ask this of me? It is too much.' He is wrestling with himself. We are alone in the upper room of Mathias Ben Ahab, which is used by the disciples for the purposes of meeting and receiving teaching.

He doubts his ability to fulfil that which is asked of him.

He is loved by many but for each one who loves him there are many who would wish him harm, who envy him or would desire to use his powers to their own ends. There are many prophets and so many of them are certain in their views and convictions, but the nature of Yeshua's wisdom is that it does not impose. By comparison with some, his wisdom seems fragile, ephemeral and no match for the certainties of others. He sometimes doubts himself every bit as much as his detractors doubt him, and at times such as this he seeks the company of those in whom he can safely confide.

Now he paces the floor, his hand over his mouth, thinking. Now I see him leaning over the table, shouting and angry, and now covering his eyes as the tears come.

A vision of the cross.

It is later on the same afternoon. He sits in a wooden chair, his weight against the back, head bowed, contemplating something that he is holding in his lap. It is a cup. The cup has contained water which he has drunk. The shutters are partially closed and the air is hot and still. There is nothing more to say. The table is set with two jugs and several cups similar to the one that Yeshua is holding.

I am standing by a window looking out on the empty street; each of us is more or less lost in our thoughts. It is he who breaks the silence, 'They will come and they will take me; not yet, but soon.'

He looks up, a question in his eyes; he wants to know that I understand. I do. He looks away, across the room, 'And when I am gone, the sun will rise on a new day.' He speaks quietly, as if addressing himself.

Josephes' sadness.

I think back over the afternoon, over the discussions we have had. It has been familiar ground, ground that we have crossed many times before. He bears the Christ but he is still a man and what man lives without fear, without hopes and without the need of the love of others?

So often he feels torn, torn between the love of God and the warmth of people. He loves God and he loves people but he also knows where the love of God will ultimately lead, for God is asking of him what he has asked of no man before.

Many have heard the words of the Messiah or seen his miracles but few indeed have seen his suffering. There are times when he cries aloud for the burden to be lifted from his shoulders, and to listen to his anguish at times such as these, knowing that the most rare and beautiful flower in creation will be taken from us, is too terrible to bear.

Josephes reflects on his relationship with Yeshua.

The table again, the upper room. It is dark now, it would seem that we have spent the better part of the afternoon here talking. There are oil lamps on the table and they are lit, each one casting as much light as a large candle. We have talked of many things in the time we have shared together but this memory is not of the content of the discussion but of the nature of our relationship.

It is said that we are like brothers and this is true but only in the sense of the familiarity that exists between us. There are no secrets, all is shared, and there is little of the competitiveness that can so often mar the relationship between brothers. The understanding is deeper, but we are like brothers in the sense that nothing is held back or hidden from the other. He knows me as he knows himself and I know him in the same way; strengths, weaknesses, irritations and fears, each knows the heart of the other.

In the tunnels under Jerusalem.

I can see ripples from a drop of water moving outward in a small dark pool. There is only the light of a lantern here. We are in the maze of tunnels underneath the city, and they are cool and damp in places with the occasional pool fed from above. Rumours and superstition abound about this place and few will venture in. We became acquainted with the tunnels as children, Yeshua having no fear of such places, and now that he is back in the city he comes here for the peace, solitude and refuge that they offer. It is hard to imagine the noise of the city in the stillness of this place. Our voices echo as we softly speak.

Neither of us are in the city much; lately his work takes him far and wide and my duties require both a presence in Cyprus and business trips as well. He and a band of followers spend much of their time with the sick and the poor, for such as these, he feels, are more open to receiving what he has to give than are the cynics and sophisticates of the city.

Look deep into the dark corners of your hearts; I will be there.

Yeshua is leading a small group of followers through the outskirts of Jerusalem. He leads us into the desert. It is a particularly unattractive area, strewn with rocks, weeds and rubbish. Nobody in the group can understand why he has brought us here; there are far more beautiful locations for discourse that surround the city.

When he has found a suitable spot he turns to face the group and one of our number asks why he has brought us to such a God-forsaken place. He answers simply, 'It is not possible for God to forsake this place, nor any other place on earth nor any of His creatures or plants or His people or their actions. Why should He forsake what He created? It is only man that can turn his back on those things that displease him. God cannot forsake, but He can feel grief, whereas what man cannot suffer, he forsakes.

'Had it not been for me none of you would have sought this place out, and you wonder why I brought you here. If you look into your hearts are there not places just such as this? Where all that displeases you, all that pains and shames you is stored and buried out of sight, just as this place is shunned by the city? And yet is not the Son of Man standing here in this forsaken spot? If you look into your hearts, deep into the dark corners of your hearts, believe me, I will be there.'

While studying the Torah, Josephes muses on Yeshua's teachings.

It is night-time. I am sitting at a desk, my fingers pressing into my eyes. I am tired from reading the Torah. It is late in life to return to this study but since Yeshua's return from India my interest in all things spiritual has awakened: meditation, prayer and study. But I struggle with the written teachings of our tradition in the same way as I struggled as a young man. To listen to Yeshua is a mixed blessing, too. When he talks he does not issue rules for behaviour or laws or history but speaks directly to the heart of the matter. Something which makes my own efforts to understand seem all the more laborious.

At least now I can see the sense of Jewish thinking. Yeshua explains things simply and when he does, the teachings I grew up with are revealed as containing a depth and elegance that is quite beautiful – though it is hard for me to liberate such depth from the script in front of me. If these words were the window to a room, then Yeshua would be like a light on the inside shining out, and those of us who listen would be looking in, awed.

From one point of view it could be said that my studies are successful. To be able to recognise that there is a difference between the source and the outworkings of that source is an achievement, even if I cannot always differentiate one from the other. Yeshua talks of the Creator as his father, but he means that the Creator is father of all things and not just his personal father. It is a revolutionary concept that challenges notions of good and evil; it also suggests that we are born of perfection and not of woe.

While these ideas are impossible to prove, they are too exquisite to dismiss out of hand, and the more I think about it the more sense it makes. The Creator is what is common to all the creatures in the world, even to the world itself – nobody is separate. As Yeshua is fond of stating, we all share the same air and none can survive without it, yet nobody can see it and nobody can prove it. Just like the Father.

A gift from a great teacher.

I see Yeshua, calling out to someone above the heads of those who are assembled. This is not a public group; all who are here are of the diciplehood. Yeshua is pointing and waving with his right hand as he shouts to Simon Peter for instructions about where we are going. In his left hand, which is by his side, he is holding a small clear quartz crystal, about two or three inches long and three quarters of an inch thick. His thumb is on the top pointing towards the tip which is exposed. When the location has been decided we set off towards a small hillside. It has been used for the purposes of teaching before because, when all are seated, the slope allows everyone a good clear view of the Master.

As he talks I am aware of how he holds the quartz crystal in his hand. Such things are not unusual to me, our family deals in minerals. He does not draw attention to it nor does it appear to be significant as far as the teaching goes; he holds it as one would hold any small personal possession that brings comfort while talking. When the lesson is over, the crowd has dispersed and some of us are walking home together, I ask him about the crystal. He hands it to me and tells me that it was a gift. It is heavier than I expected and smoky, with a smooth oily texture that has been imparted to the stone from endless handling. Holding it gives me a feeling of wellbeing and security. Yeshua says that it was given to him by a teacher he met in India and that it was in turn a gift from his teacher. Yeshua says that he does not know how many generations of teachers have held the stone but he thinks that it is a great many. I hand it back, realising that I have just had in my hand a token of great spiritual significance.

To know his love – a healing.

I can see a man on his back in a wagon. The wagon is being drawn by a donkey and is accompanied by several men. As they proceed, the leader stops those he passes, asking where the healer is. Some look at him as if he is crazy, some ignore him and some give news of what they know. Through all this activity he has attracted the attention of a number of children and people who have nothing better to do with their time and who are following the wagon, turning the whole thing into an untidy procession. I am struck by his determination and the dignity which he maintains despite the rabble who have attached themselves to his quest.

I approach him and am immediately struck by his face. It is a face that has known great hardship, lined and coloured by exposure to the elements and yet the soft blue eyes are possessed of a gentleness and understanding. His love for the sick man must be great for it is clear from his clothing that he has travelled many miles. I explain that I know where he can find the man he is looking for, not now but later, and seek his assurance that he will come only with his sick friend if I give him the information he seeks. He agrees to this and I make arrangements to meet him later in the day.

There are many gathered already when the man arrives, carrying his friend like a child in his arms. It is not much of a burden because the sick man has been the victim of a wasting disease. The blue-eyed one has been true to his word and has come without his entourage. I can see clearly the sick man as he enters the room, his skin yellowed, head lolling against the chest of his friend, dry lips drawn back from his teeth. It strikes me that perhaps a miracle has already happened in that a body as wasted as this one can still support life.

Yeshua looks up and makes his way directly to the man. He focuses his attention not on the sick one, though, but on the man who is carrying him, who is explaining to Yeshua how far he has come searching for him. There is a pause as Yeshua looks intently at the man and then says, 'Your friend will recover, but it is not you who brought him to me, but he who brought you to me. He has been your guide.'

The man is visibly stunned by these words; they seem to touch a very deep chord. Such a response is not unusual for it is my belief that there has never been, and never again will be, one who can touch people as Yeshua does.

Those who meet him and are touched by him are changed for all eternity. He cannot change his own destiny but he changes the destiny of all who meet him. Once his gentle spirit touches the heart of those who come, they are awakened as never before and they know absolutely and in an instant what their ultimate goal is: to know this love as their own.

A meeting with Timothy.
He beckons me over. He is standing on a ridge or the brow of a hill pointing down over the other side. I climb up to him and look down where he is pointing; there is a flock of sheep, some with bells ringing, and tended by two shepherds. They are simple men and poor by their appearance but both are smiling broadly up at Yeshua – they know him and are pleased to see him.

We walk down towards them and the one who is nearest walks forward to greet us. He is a young man, bare-legged and barefoot carrying a staff and wearing the skins of the animals he tends. He is short and wiry with a wide mouth, full lips and even white teeth. He has brown eyes and masses of curly black hair.

Yeshua introduces us: his name is Timothy and he is one of the greater group of disciples. He has a beautiful nature, a childlike guilelessness, almost feminine in his demeanour. We talk for some minutes and during this time Timothy has occasion to keep the sheep together, which he does by throwing stones on the opposite side of the direction he wishes the sheep to move. He does this with a casual but uncannily accurate and powerful throw. He possesses some of the qualities of Yeshua himself: confident at the same time as being shy, and I imagine that he would be just as happy and fulfilled in the company of people, sheep or nature.

A teaching.
I am looking down on a man's head. He has curly black shiny hair and about his shoulders is a dark blue toga. I seem to be in a crowd, somehow tiered, maybe standing or sitting on the side of a steep hill. There are a good many of us gathered here, mostly men, maybe thirty or forty in number, and all are known as disciples.

Yeshua is teaching though it is not the content of what he is teaching that is of importance in this memory. To separate the words from the man is like looking upon a statue, a likeness in stone: it can be very beautiful but it is still hard and lacking in life and emphasis.

As he speaks his voice is calm and loving, and there is a tangible energy of love in what he speaks that enables him to say quite difficult and challenging things without raising the defences of the listener; his words are spoken with great compassion. It is difficult to know whether it is the words or the way that they are spoken that is so meaningful, but perhaps words are like boats: they sail the sea, they look the same, but one might carry gold, while another carries weapons.

The birth of Japheth.
I am holding a baby, newly born. On the bed below me is my exhausted smiling wife and next to me is my mother. I pass the baby to her; he is a boy and she takes him from me with tears in her eyes. He is our third child after Jacob and Mary. I stand beside my mother and look into his eyes. He is beautiful and he touches me in a way that is different from the first two children. My mother senses my feeling and says simply, 'He has Yeshua's eyes.'

Josephes grows more content with quiet places, nature and his own company.
Heat, and the dry wind that blows off the desert. I am spending a moment alone. Although rebellious as a younger man against the religious and social constraints that were placed upon me, I have more recently turned my

attention to meditation. This is partly through the influence of Yeshua and partly because my need to make an independent mark on the world has waned somewhat. I have accepted more and more that I am of my family, of my class and of my religion. It has occurred to me of late that had I been born to a different family I might have fulfilled my father's wishes and made good material for the priesthood but it is of no matter now.

With more acceptance of who I am has come the desire to explore my own spirituality and to my daily delight I find it there, unorthodox and deep. I find myself drawn more and more to the quiet places, to nature and to my own company. It is a great treasure to be alone and content with myself and no mean achievement given the events and people that have surrounded me. So I sit here with the heat, the stillness and the quiet for company, for a few moments perfectly content.

Josephes helps a man who has been flogged.
Jerusalem. A man's back is bared. It is a strong and muscular back, deep brown from hard labour under the sun. The man is forced to kneel, and he does not go down willingly. The lash is laid to his back without mercy, several soldiers taking turns lest their efforts should flag from fatigue. I watch his muscles tense in anticipation of the pain of each stroke. I remember my own beating – compared to this man they were merciful with me. They continue relentlessly until his muscles remain limp to the whip, then let him drop heavily to the ground. They have broken him physically and maybe mentally, too. It is not difficult for them; in matters of punishment they are expert, they know exactly what they are doing.

It will be very difficult for him to recover from this, though – that is, if he is not dead. I ask one of the onlookers what he has done to deserve such a beating and they reply that the man offered resistance to Caesar. That could mean anything, and frequently does.

The man lies motionless, the crowd starts to move away. No-one wants to run the risk of being associated with one who has been publicly flogged. I wait until they are virtually all gone, then a woman steps forward and crouches by the man's head. I step forward to help but she starts back as I approach. 'It is all right, sister, I mean him no harm.' She relaxes and accepts my help – she has to, there is no way that she can carry this man to safety alone. As I kneel beside her I realise that he is too big for me also; he will have to find his feet if he is not to lie here all day. At least they have spared his life, though I doubt that they care.

I put my hand gently on his head and call on my cousin's assistance. I have already learned something of healing from my father and Yeshua has taught me to do this. He groans and turns his head towards me. His brow is broad and he is heavily bearded, with blue eyes. 'Come my friend, you must help us carry you.' I am surprised at the strength and determination left in his body. He raises himself on his forearms and with our help gets unsteadily to his feet. I can see now why the soldiers were so hard on him: if he could stand up straight he would be a head taller than me. He leans heavily on us both as we set off, led by the woman.

The going is hard but not for long; it would appear that the man was dragged from his home to the nearest public place for the flogging. It is not unusual; the humiliation and the example is all the more effective if the miscreant is whipped in front of family, neighbours and friends. But still, it means that we do not have so far to go to get him home. Home turns out to be a sparse room off an alleyway and once the door is closed the woman breaks down in tears despite her attempts to remain dignified in front of me. I can see that she is embarrassed, though she has no need to be, and she struggles to regain her composure. We lay her man face down on the bed virtually unconscious, and she busies herself preparing water and fresh linen.

As she tends his back I ask her what his crime was and

she lowers her eyes, suspicious of my concern, still not trusting me. I wait until her eyes meet mine and tell her that I, too, have been flogged by the Romans. She glances at my hands, which are soft and elegant, not the hands of a working man, and I can feel her judgment in the look. 'And what was your crime?' she asks. 'Chasing women,' I answer honestly.

She can see from my eyes that I am telling the truth and she softens her attitude. That men are powerless against their passions she can understand. 'He spoke out against the Romans.' 'Then he is lucky to be alive,' I reply, 'and he will not work for some time.'

I stand up to take my leave and before going open my purse and offer her some money. Immediately she bristles and becomes contemptuous. 'Take it, sister, lest your pride kill you both.' She pauses, her eyes on mine, then takes the money, but I can see that it costs her dearly to do so. 'I will send you healing salts, the same that healed my back.' As I turn toward the door I hear her offer her thanks.

Walking home, I think about the events of the morning. There are many like this in Jerusalem, poor Jews, frightened and angry. They see the Romans as the cause of their problems. For many this hatred is with some justification, while for others it is a question of having someone to blame for their own insufficiencies. For me it is more complicated. I am a Jew from a very wealthy family and to some extent our continued wealth is consequent upon our relationship with the Roman authorities. On the other hand it is not a consequence of this relationship alone, nor is it based on prejudice and anger but rather more on birth, opportunity and hard work. I feel a loyalty to my kin but there are times when this loyalty should be put first and times when such loyalty would only lead to more destruction. There is little point in fighting an enemy that is obviously more powerful, and while they are more powerful I believe it is better to turn my attention to the enemy within.

Josephes reflects on people's attitudes towards Yeshua.

I can see Yeshua's hands over food, giving a blessing. As we eat he talks of his travels. There are now none who are close to him that do not absolutely accept his spiritual authority. He is just recently returned from one of his journeys amongst the sick. Although he is supported like no other by the strength of his calling these journeys take their toll and he is deeply tired. He is tired not just in his body but also by what he sees. It is not those who need his help and who gratefully accept it that cause his fatigue, but the attitude of those who feel that they do not need it to those that do.

Both Yeshua and those he tends are so often treated with contempt, suspicion and unkindness. It is the unspoken pain of those that mock that takes its toll, those whose hearts are hardened by their own despair, who are too cynical to reach out, who would rather doubt than trust. Those who feel that their humanness and vulnerability is a curse rather than a gift from God. Those that would rather wound than feel wounded, who when they see the light that shines from his eyes, would sooner put out his eyes than question why they cannot gaze into them. And never does he turn them away.

To give and receive.

I can see a stoppered clay flask. The stopper is drawn and fresh clear water is poured on to a pair of dirty feet, splashing on to the parched earth and turning it dark. Under the dirt the feet are quite beautiful, although cut and sore. The feet belong to Yeshua. Since his return from India I have seldom known him wear sandals; no matter how sharp or rocky the terrain, how thorny or smooth, he walks as if on soft green grass. As a consequence of this his feet are always in terrible condition and seen by his followers as being in constant need of attention.

Although he never complains or asks for help he is never short of it, for those with whom he travels or meets cannot bear to think of him suffering. Despite his abilities, where his own comfort is concerned he remains stubbornly a man, and will not lift a finger to effect the healing on himself that he offers to others. It is just as well, for there is even on occasion competition to perform the washing and anointing with healing oils. He is not churlish enough to turn such help away; indeed he positively lights up with the attention, for it is in his nature not only to give of his love but to delight in receiving it.

Speaking the simple truth.
Jerusalem. There is a group of us accompanying Yeshua on a short journey; some are new to his teachings, some are not. As he walks he speaks, and his words leave a trail of destruction in his wake. His speech is like hearing beautiful music from a forgotten land, a land that is the true home of us all. The beauty of what he says reveals the false gods of fame, wealth and power for what they are, and leaves them in ruins. And how does he manage this? Not with blade or stone or by force of will, but by speaking the simple truth with absolute humility, despite any consequences that may accrue. He leaves hope, devastation and yearning in the hearts of those that listen, that will give them as much cause to curse him as to love him.

A parting.
It is the evening, just before darkness settles over the city, and we have reached the site of the water cistern. It has been a long walk and we are dusty and tired from the road. We each lean forward and wash our faces in cupped hands; I can see the drops of water clearly clinging to Yeshua's beard and face as he rises from the water. We sit on the parapet wall and lean back for a few moments before going our separate ways – there is no need to speak. I am due to return to Cyprus in the morning.

A journey to hear Yeshua speak.
Polished copper fittings on a saddle level with my face. The

saddle is on a camel and on the saddle is seated a man looking down at me. I am amongst a group of desert dwellers, travelling people. Many mistrust them but I have spent time amongst them with my father and have learned something of their ways. I am asking directions from the leader; he is Arab and speaks in Aramaic as he points the way. I thank him and make my way back to my travelling companion who is holding my horse. I had dismounted and approached the Arabs on foot as a mark of respect, just as they would have done had they reason to approach me. I mount my horse and wave to them as we set off toward some low hills that are not too distant. I will take my leave of my companion when we enter the hills and travel on alone towards my destination.

I am in a small village in the country which is built on the side of a hill. The village is in a mountainous area and is overlooked by one particularly large mountain in the distance. The houses are small and humble but not poor; they are well preserved and welcoming. There is one particular house that I am making for. Due to the construction of the house and the fact that it is built on the side of a fairly steep road, it is necessary to descend several steps to enter the front door which is open.

Inside, the room is simple, with walls that are yellowish ochre from the smoke of the fireplace. There is a window on the right with a stout cloth to pull over it to keep the weather out. There are several pieces of utilitarian furniture: chairs, a table and a bed and chest, and there is also a cooking area by the fireplace. But for the moment the room is empty of people so I sit at the table to wait. I look around this room which I know well and where I have spent many happy hours but my reminiscences are interrupted by the arrival of the owner. He is coarsely dressed in the manner of a shepherd, which is his occupation. I stand as he enters and greets me effusively. He bids me go before him to the house of his mother.

His mother lives in the same village in a similar but slightly larger and more comfortable dwelling. She is warm and welcoming, and the house is far more homely than her son's with the smell of food cooking and with fabrics as well as animal skins on the furniture. It is not long before we are seated at the table eating and sharing news of friends and family. This young man is Timothy who Yeshua introduced me to. We have discovered a natural affinity for one another and a firm friendship has developed between us. He is one of the disciples – not of the twelve but, like me and my father, one who is drawn to the teachings and is accepted as a follower of the Way.

The meal is eaten and we are sitting and talking quietly, waiting. There is one more person expected, another of the disciples who has agreed to meet us here. We do not have to wait too long before he appears in the doorway, out of breath and sweating. He greets us, apologising for his lateness and is offered food which he accepts gratefully. Now our small party is complete and as soon as our friend has finished his food and has had a chance to rest awhile we gather our things and set off into the hills that surround this area to meet with other members of the group.

There is a particular village on the shores of the Sea of Galilee where Yeshua often stays. Bounded by inhospitable hills, remote and untouched by the outside world, it is populated by followers of the teachings. Many of them are Essene, villagers of long-standing, and there are also many who have settled in the village from far-off places in order to share their lives with like-minded people. They are quiet, discreet and always welcoming to true seekers so their home is an ideal meeting place for Yeshua and his followers. It is to this destination that we are headed. Between us we have but one horse, the chestnut mare that my father bought me. Our companion and I ride on her back whilst Timothy takes the reins before us. He is familiar with the narrow mountain paths that we have to traverse and is more comfortable on foot.

It is night-time and we have reached our destination. We have eaten and I am making my way across the village square towards a small house set against a hillside. I have been looking forward with some anticipation to this moment. I enter the house and go through to the back, where I pass through a doorway into a large cavern that has been hewn out of the rock. This hall has been used for generations for the purposes of teaching. The roof is domed slightly and there is a raised dais at the end furthest from the entrance. There are no windows and the whole space is lit by a great number of oil lanterns which cast a beautiful glow on the light rock of the walls and ceiling. The atmosphere of the place is one of profound stillness and peace.

It is the rule within the community that when the hall is not being used for formal teaching anyone within the village may gather for debate or the sharing of ideas or teaching. Such discourses are open to anyone who wishes to join in. There may at one time be two or three groups of several people talking or meditating together. If one should choose to be alone the dais is designated as an area where the occupant will be undisturbed by those others who are gathered. If one of the elders or a visiting teacher is present then the room is often filled to bursting.

I am hoping that Yeshua will be here already. He is not expecting me since it was only at the last minute that I was able to make arrangements to come. When I enter my hopes are rewarded: there are but three in the hall – the slender, slightly stooped figure of Yeshua with his back to me, and before him two others. Yeshua turns and looks over his shoulder towards me, the initial look of surprise turns to a smile as he recognises me, and my heart melts in an instant. Since his ministry has begun I can never quite believe that he will need my company as much as I need his, but always he does.

It is late. We are in a small room – the guest room in the

house of one of the villagers – which has a bed set against one wall and a chair and chest against the other. Yeshua is sitting on the bed and I am in the chair. We have been talking for some time now. It seems such a long time since we last saw one another; his work has taken him far and wide and I have had my own family and the estate in Cyprus to attend to.

He talks of his journeys, as a man rather than as a teacher, glad of the opportunity to be no more than a cousin and a friend. He talks of his progress, of how the Christ is not yet constant within him but comes forth when needed. He talks of the burden of teaching and leading his followers, of how they want to see and hear the Master, the Christed one who inspires them, not the man who has the same failings as they do. It is not always easy for him to bear such expectations, to keep his own spirits high when he knows only too well the price he will ultimately pay for his work.

There are many who look upon Yeshua, who see him shine, who see him as the chosen vessel for the power of God and, in seeing his beauty and grace, they both love him and secretly wish that they had it for themselves. I have felt this way myself from time to time but I also see what they do not: the other side, the anguish and torment that such demands create in him. He must constantly summon the strength to go on, dredge the very depths of his resources to continue. And all this he keeps private.

To see the Christ emerge from within the man is a privilege indeed, but to be trusted with the knowledge of the human price he pays for this I consider to be an even greater privilege. For he needs love, too; not the idealised love that shines from the eyes of devotees, nor even the love that pours from the hearts of those who see the Christ, but the love of those whom he can trust with his own misgivings.

The lamp is low and the room is still and quiet, nothing

stirs save for the sound of our breathing. Yeshua is lying on the bed; sleep has embraced him and mercifully lifted the burden from his shoulders for the night. I remain in the chair awhile, enfolded by the quietness before retiring. I cast my mind over the events of the day, over the evening and what we have shared, and the contrast between this peacefully sleeping form and the anguish and need that filled him earlier. Somewhere at my back I can feel the wheels of destiny turning and I know that inevitably they will come full circle, but for this moment all is peace, and this peace is all that matters.

I think back over our lives as I watch him sleep. We have always been close but it has not always been an easy relationship. We grew up together as equals but he had far more potential than I, and while I rejoiced at his skills, from time to time my heart also burned with envy. To some he appears as no more than an ordinary man, they judge him as they would judge other men, expect no more of him than they would of themselves and they are right to, for in many ways he is no more than an ordinary man. But he also stands outside the ordinary, he is both in and out of the drama of life, subject to it totally and yet beyond it, and he tells us that we are capable of this, too, that what is his is also ours. It gives such hope and yet sometimes it is this very hope that makes me so furious. Like the beggar who is told by a wealthy merchant that he, also, has the ability to be rich.

I look at him sleeping and think back to this morning, to the love in his eyes when he saw me enter the hall, and wonder how I am able to feel such extremes of emotion. How strange this man is, a living god who still needs to put his arm on the shoulder of his friends for support. Such humility is beyond my understanding but perhaps he knows that the merchant needs the beggar more than the beggar needs the merchant.

It is morning and I am in the great meeting room. I am

among the throng that has assembled and Yeshua is on the dais receiving those who come forward for healing or blessing or to touch his hands, for now the man is filled again with light. Beside Yeshua is a respected elder of the community who, at an opportune moment, raises his hands for silence and attention. He leads the group in meditation and prayer and then formally introduces Yeshua who in fact is known to all but a few.

Yeshua delivers a beautiful talk, carefully crafted and tailored to the needs and aspirations of the group. He talks of the true meaning of community, that it is not economic or primarily for protection nor even is it to do with proximity, for true community is a state of heart, an understanding of truth and love.

From within the audience I can feel the atmosphere change as he speaks. What started as an excited rather fragmented group calms and becomes serene as Yeshua's words call forth from the depths of each one the very love that he is describing. That which was buried in the breast of each begins to shine and touch those who are standing alongside and that which was but a dream for most becomes a living reality.

It is morning again and time for me to return. I am to make my journey home to Jerusalem where my duties await me. Timothy is to accompany me to the home of his mother, where we will spend the night, and on the next day he will return to the community while I will travel onwards alone. Timothy brings the horse as I bid farewell to my friends and especially to my cousin. I am not one for prolonging farewells and so without too much ado we both mount the mare and set off on our journey.

It is a long and difficult ride along the mountain paths and I am glad to feel the warmth and weight of my friend at my back. We have in the past spent many hours together and we understand each other's moods and feelings very deeply. I feel empty from the parting and yet at the same time full with the words of my cousin. In some ways I would like nothing more than to join the band of follow-ers that accompany Yeshua on his travels but I have my own family and commitments to care for. It is also the case that much of the finance required to provide for Yeshua's ministry is found from the Arimathean family coffers and so there is always more than one way to help.

As Timothy and I ride we discuss the implications and ramifications of what we have learned during our stay, enjoying the clean mountain air and the companionship of the journey.

It is early morning and the air is crisp and cool as I prepare my horse for the onward journey. It is with a heavy heart that I bid farewell to Timothy and his mother and set off on the road home. The going is quick so it is not long before I find myself descending out of the mountains and into the heat of the day.

It is a long day of riding and when I finally arrive at our Jerusalem home I am thankful to hand the reins of my horse to a servant who will take care of her. As I approach the house I reflect on the contrast between the opulence and wealth of our lifestyle compared to the humbleness of Timothy's, but even more I am struck by how unimpor-tant it is at the moment and the absolute feeling of equal-ity that comes from opening the heart.

I make my way up the stairs to my father's room. He is out of his chair and heading towards me as I enter. He takes my forearms in his hands and leads me to a chair opposite his. He pushes a jug of wine and a cup towards me and I take a little sip. He does not want to press me but I can see he is desperate for news of Yeshua and the disci-ples so I waste no time in unravelling my story. He listens attentively as I do, nodding from time to time but never interrupting, and when I describe Yeshua's talk in the great hall a tear comes to his eye.

The light of the world.
I am back in Cyprus thinking back on the trip, recalling

the time I spent with my cousin. I recall us walking slowly, strolling, Yeshua walking beside me at my left side and as we walk, we talk. It is late in the afternoon and he talks as the initiate. He is so many things – cousin, son, brother, nephew, uncle – but on that evening all are fused with the Master. He talks of light and, gesturing towards the trees and rocks that we are passing, tries to explain the vast scheme of which they are but a visible part.

He talks of the lights that govern them and the lights that create them. The world, he explains, is a creation of light but it is like the world at night: the light is there, the animals can see it but man cannot. He talks of man's inability to see the light in terms of exile, that there are a great many who are in exile from the light. Not because they have been excluded but because they have turned their backs on it. They entered the darkness out of curiosity, out of a desire to know it, but where there is darkness there is fear and fear blinds the eyes and fogs the memory, so they cannot find their way back.

He talks of those who have forgotten as being like those who have no homeland, the poor and the homeless in the world – they see the wealth of others but they feel powerless and do not know how to obtain it for themselves. He says that these ones must be fed, because they have forgotten how to raise the food to their own lips. When the food is offered and their trust is won and when they eat from the hands of those who have, the taste will be more haunting and beautiful than any food that a wealthy man, who has always had plenty, has ever tasted, and it will awaken their hunger for more. This, he says, is his purpose: to feed the hungry.

The lesson of Christ.
I can see his face now, illuminated by a candle flame which he is watching intently, just as we did when we were children. From where I am seated at the table the candle is out of my line of sight, and it looks to me as if the light is shining out of his face rather than reflected from it. There

is such gentleness in his expression. Occasionally he looks slightly to the side to speak quietly to a companion, and I watch his lips move and see the light in his eyes. I cannot hear the words that are being spoken but I do not need to. There are many who would hear the words of Christ, who would seek to write down what he speaks but if the words were important I am sure that he would have been a writer himself rather than a healer. The lesson of Christ is his life.

Josephes' longing.

I have been on Cyprus for several months. I am needed here, Japheth is still very young and Ruth needs my help, and there are business matters to attend to. But my heart is on the mainland with my cousin; I think of him constantly. Although Ruth senses my longing it is hard for her to let me go. Finally she can bear it no longer and urges me to go.

Back to the mainland.

I am walking along a dry dusty road, pale chalky-coloured stone. To my left there are crops growing and ahead of me I can see low white buildings. It is early morning. I pass the buildings and the crops give way to scrub and stones. The road steepens and climbs into hills and narrow gorges. It is a hard climb and I am thankful for the water I am carrying. Finally the road levels out and the hills to my right give way to the broad expanse of the Sea of Galilee below me. I pause for rest and refreshment and look back down the road at the green fields far below me. I am returning to the community where I last met Yeshua. Word has been sent and he is expecting me, so I press on.

It has been a hard day's walking but finally I am at my destination. I am on the shore of the Sea of Galilee, dirty, tired and sweaty. The water looks inviting so I take off my sandals; the smooth rocks are hot under my feet as I make my way to the water's edge to bathe them. I sit for some time just resting and feeling the cool water. We had arranged to meet at sundown and I estimate that there is about an hour to go, so I walk on the rocks, in and out of the water, my feet leaving dark wet prints behind me.

As the sun starts to go down I begin to get a little anxious, wondering whether I have come on the right day or at the right time. Then someone approaches – a young man in his twenties who asks my name. 'I am Josephes,' I reply, and he bids me follow him. I pull on my sandals and follow him. He walks quickly and now I have rested, my limbs are stiff so I struggle to keep up with him. We walk along the shore road until it turns away around a rocky and sheer part of the shoreline. To our right is a narrow path leading down to the shore. The light is almost gone so we take great care as we make our way down. Finally we round a corner and there is Yeshua with three others, two men and a woman. He steps forward immediately and we embrace: 'Josephes, how I have waited for this moment.' I reply, 'And I, too.'

He apologises for not coming to meet me personally but, he explains, it is too dangerous for him to be seen in daylight in these parts. The stars are beginning to shine and I can just make out a fishing boat moored not far from the shore. We are ushered into a smaller boat and ferried out to it.

It is a trip that takes about three hours before we are at our destination. The wind is low and all hands are needed to speed us on our way so conversation is limited; even so, I pick up a sense of danger and urgency amongst our companions. Eventually we arrive at the community and are welcomed by those who have been waiting. Many of them I know well and we spend a little time exchanging greetings. They are aware that my time is limited, though, and before long Yeshua and I are left quietly alone to walk in the cool starlight.

He asks for news of the family. He dare not come to Jerusalem himself, and I share what I know. He listens carefully, nodding occasionally. He has an air of both deep peace and gravity about him. He tells me of his travels and of the community here, of the disciples and of his work but the words are only part of our communication. There is that certain easy familiarity, a knowing that always feels to me like a homecoming.

We lapse into silence and stand with our backs against a big, warm smooth rock and look up at the sky. The heavens are arrayed brilliantly; millions upon millions of stars look down at us. When we were younger we would spend hours like this in the desert or on Cyprus, just looking up into the night sky.

Suddenly there is a brilliant shooting star – not the ordinary kind, that burns for a second and then dies but one that streaks across the sky burning with such intensity that it seems to cut the very heavens open. My thoughts are interrupted by Yeshua who asks softly, 'You remember?' There is something in his voice. As children we always believed that a shooting star meant something: a birth, a death or an angel visiting. 'I remember.' I look over to where he is leaning and feel his eyes searching mine through the darkness. 'The time draws close, Josephes. I need your strength.'

We walk slowly back to the dwellings, his arm in mine and my heart bursting with love for this man, who asks for my strength and yet without whom I would be as lost and as weak as a child.

A meeting.

It is some months later and I have not returned to the mainland since I last saw my cousin. My father is here on Cyprus with Yeshua who has come for the peace and to regenerate himself. His work is ceaseless and he drives himself without rest. His followers demand as much from him as those he heals.

We are walking in the countryside with Amos, my brother's son who lives with us here. Yeshua talks of the pressures on him, of politics. There are those who would have him claim a right to the throne of David. They have seen his power and speculate how it might be used to overthrow the Roman rule and set the Jewish nation free again. On the other hand there are those who are content to follow his teaching, who understand that the true kingdom has nothing to do with the Romans. And closer to home there are those within our own community, amongst the Sanhedrin, where some see him as a trouble-maker while others wish to follow his teaching.

I watch my father as he listens; he looks old and I see the alarm and concern in his face as he listens to his nephew. He is known within the Sanhedrin as a supporter of Yeshua's work and is well aware of the feelings that he evokes in those he comes into contact with. He suggests that Yeshua stay here, on Cyprus, until things have calmed down but Yeshua speaks softly. He will return.

The love of the Father.
We are alone, it is late and we are standing in the moon-light on the shore near the house where we played as chil-dren. The waters are gentle and the breeze is soft and warm. I am expressing the same concerns as my father, entreating him to stay awhile with us, where he is safe. He listens attentively to what I have to say but my heart is not in it; I know that his mind is made up and I am only going through the motions and we lapse into silence. Eventually he speaks quietly and with certainty, to the sea rather than directly to me, 'You must understand that my life is not my own – I must go where my Father directs me to go. I am in His hands and His hands will take me to the mainland tomorrow.'

I watch the side of his face; he seems so peaceful. He turns slightly towards me, 'Beloved Josephes, do not fear for me. Do you remember when we were young and we would lie for hours off this very shore in our boat?' I nod. 'Do you remember the way the sea would roll underneath us and support us? We felt so safe in our little boat.'

It is true; we had a trust in the sea that was born of innocence. We felt that nothing could tip us out, and even if it had we wouldn't have cared for we were equally at home in the water. 'I feel His love supporting me now like the sea did then, gentle but firm. He does not fear for me.' I feel the tears on my cheeks as he speaks, and we look out to sea without speaking.

The return.
With several others I am helping my father and Yeshua into the large boat that will take them back to the mainland. We are loading in the supplies that they will need and some items of cargo. When all is fast we embrace, say our farewells and I step off the boat on to the small jetty. The sails are hoisted, the wind catches them and the boat slowly pulls away.

I watch them go, waving back to me at first and then applying themselves to the tasks of sailing. Occasionally I can see one of their faces turn white in the distance as they look back towards the shore. When they are finally no more than a dot in the distance I pull my cloak around me and make my way back up to the house. I do not know it but it is the last time I will see my cousin alive.

Chapter 8

News of the crucifixion

A constriction in my throat, sadness or grief, but I cannot let go to the tears. Grey pyramid-shaped rocks. It is evening and the light has almost gone. I have come here to be alone. My grief turns to numbness as the moon rises. I am aware of the water lapping against the rocks. I am in the small bay near the family home on Cyprus; the bay that was the scene of so much lightheartedness and joy in childhood is now companion to my grief.

I have just heard news of the crucifixion. My cousin is dead. The man I loved more than any other has been killed on the cross. I can accept the words but not what they mean. The feelings come in waves, and each time the tears come I clench my fists in rage. If my tears are spilt I will have to accept that it is true.

There will be no sleep for me tonight, no sleep and no comfort until I have made my way to Jerusalem to find out for myself.

The journey to Jerusalem.
I am sitting in a white tunic. Although it is morning the sun is already hot but I am oblivious to it. I am waiting for the boat to come and take me to the mainland. It is the morning after the news of Yeshua's death and I have not slept. At least the physical tiredness has stopped my mind from working so fast. The numbness I am feeling is comforting but I know that it is temporary; behind it is rage at my father. Why did he not stop it? Though I cannot entertain it, behind the rage is a feeling of guilt. I should have been there, I should have done more, I let him down.

Josephes despairs.
The steps down to the tomb in the garden at our Jerusalem home. The door is open, the tomb is bare, cool white chalk-coloured rock. I stand outside uncomprehending. There are some who say that he has been seen

again but there are many, many more who actually saw him die. The house is silent, still with grief.

The tomb is simply hewn from the rock upon which the house stands. Despite all that has passed, it is peaceful inside. There are two broad shelves running down either side from the entrance with a deep walkway between, about one metre wide. There is a close-fitting stone door. I am sitting on the right-hand side, looking at the place where my cousin was laid. I am numb, thinking of the times we spent together, feeling the coolness of the stone under my hands, the same stone that will in a few days support my remains and the remains of my son.

It seems to me that the rabble won; the lowest and crudest in man overcame the highest and best and destroyed it. Does light hurt the eyes of sinners so much that they must put it out? My thoughts are dark and bitter. I have not just lost a beloved cousin but, standing here in the garden, I become convinced that this is a triumph of darkness over light and that the light has lost. As with many others, the significance of the resurrection will take a long time to dawn on me.

Josephes visits Golgotha in despair.
Golgotha, dark rocks. A barren hill where every kind of abomination takes place: whipping, crucifixion, mutilation and torture. The air reeks of suffering and death. This must be the most God-forsaken spot in Israel and yet I am drawn back here. Perhaps it is because this place mirrors so perfectly my feelings, that inside me there is such a place, where all that is good, all that seeks to rise in love and hope is torn down and trampled. This place is no more than a monument to the destructive capacity that every man carries in his soul, a reflection of the dark hand that grips my heart this evening.

Resurrection.
I pass a donkey; I am aware of the smell and patience of a donkey with its passive eyes, ears flicking at flies. A hot dry

rocky path leading upward. Olives, olive trees. The smell of pine resin and citrus. There is a dog somewhere, faithful. The smell of sweat in the silence and hot sun. Deep grief. I am alone, thinking of Yeshua, restless, aching, tormented, wanting release – there is no peace anywhere.

The road is absolutely deserted. I am walking along it fast, determined, fists clenched. I feel nothing, I have forgotten even why or where I am walking. Behind me lies the numb grief of my family and in front of me there is nothing but emptiness.

It is only when I approach him that I notice the figure seated at the side of the road, his face obscured by his headcloth. It strikes me as strange that he should be here but I am too absorbed in my own misery to care. As I draw abreast of him he speaks my name and I stop dead in my tracks. That voice! I dare not believe, I dare not listen, I cannot move. He speaks my name again and hearing it unfreezes me. I turn slowly towards the figure as he unwinds the cloth from his face. It is Yeshua! He looks different, the skin is darker, but the eyes, the voice...

The tears stream down my face; neither of us move, not a word more is spoken, there is no need: in his eyes there is the purest love and gratitude that I have ever seen in my life. I stand transfixed as slowly he fades before my eyes and is gone.

I do not know how long I stand looking at that place. I know only that I am blessed, blessed in many ways but mostly with a deep understanding that life has no ending, it just continues in another realm.

It is difficult to describe my feelings after seeing him. Barely within my conscious mind two paths open up before me: down one path lies a future of loss, of continuing alone and inadequate to live what he has taught, even perhaps suffering similar persecution without the same inner resources. Down the other I now see a way that I can continue to be with him.

Golgotha again.
I am standing, unmoving, numbly looking at the dust. Today my meeting with Yeshua on the road seems like nothing more than a dream that serves to mock rather than console me. I doubt what I saw, argue myself out of it. What am I looking for? What do I hope to find here? What am I doing? Searching for something remaining, searching for ghosts. My mouth is dry, disbelieving.

Then comes the rage, the blind rage, the stupidity and waste of it and underneath, hardly felt, the lost hope of yesterday buried under the wrath of today. My heart is as barren as the dry dust and stones of this cursed hilltop. I pick up a rock and hurl it, tears of anger on my face. My heart fills with black bitterness, with monstrous feelings I cannot contain.

I return to my father's house and engage in a terrible confrontation: he let him die, he could have saved him. All my anger is directed at him. He stands mute and white-faced as I vent my fury and blame. No reason can penetrate my misery, nothing can bring solace – such torment and anguish is unbearable. My rage is without pity.

I know which path I should tread but in my subconscious the path of death is like a dark temptation, a forbidden fruit that is irresistible. If he exists in a realm beyond death why can I not exist there, too? Why can I not be with him there? If I, too, were to die, could I not be with him again? My mind turns over and over. I have responsibilities to my wife, to my family. I try to concentrate on these things but the thought, once entertained, will not go away. However much I try to resist it, I cannot help myself from going back and touching it again and again.

Josephes' younger son.
I see Ruth holding Japheth, our baby. I see her full head of black hair, slightly curled, and her dark skin and even white teeth. She is possessed of a natural beauty that in my eyes amounts to a kind of grace. She is dressed in an olive-green

dress which complements the colour of her skin. Japheth is more than a year old, able to stand in her lap with help. My father has taken to the desert, attending to his own grief. There is a hollow feeling inside, a numbness, and I watch the child obsessively, saying very little, as if in him I might find some of that which I have lost. Yeshua loved this one, too, and blessed him. I take the child from my wife and hold him, absorbed by his movements.

The Sea of Galilee.
My family and I are on the shore of the Sea of Galilee. It was my idea to come here, where so often we came with Yeshua. He loved this place. In my longing I have convinced myself that perhaps he will come again, I will see him again as I did on the road. If he were to come at all I know that it would be here. So we wait and we walk.

My feelings cannot be reconciled: rage, hope, despair, grief. They take turns to tear at my insides. It is a terrible thing to realise that without him there is not enough left in life to make me want to go on.

He will not come. I know that I am just putting off the inevitable. When I met him on the road after the crucifixion it was not just gratitude I saw in his eyes, it was a farewell. And now I must accept that he is gone...

A cleansing.
I am looking into the eyes of my son. This one is special, he has my eyes, my father's eyes, the eyes of Yeshua, as blue as the sky. He is looking back at me. His eyes are steady, there is no trace of fear in them.

In my arms is my son, in my heart is grief. Grief and anger. I wonder if he can feel it pressed so close against my chest. I feel the cold waters of the Sea of Galilee around my legs, cool and cleansing, cleansing the pain in my heart. He does not even flinch as his body touches the water, but I hold him tighter anyway.

In my secret dreams I wanted to give him to Yeshua. So that he could share what I shared, so that he could learn from him. Yeshua loved this one; he loved children so much and they knew it and loved him back. And now he is gone.

At the moment I slip my faith deserts me. I let go...

The water closes over our heads.

Sinking, the baby drifts from my arms. Finally my rebellious chest gives way; I feel the water fill my lungs. It is so quiet. I can see the light, grey and metallic, far above me as I sink down in the water. Death is no ogre, it is the fear of dying that distorts his fair face. As I rest back into his arms, his embrace is gentle and tender; there is no recrimination, no shame or blame, just understanding. Then there is peace, a stillness and floating and then a different light, a glimmer at first and then embracing me totally. It is soft but powerful, a light translucent gold in colour, and with a beautiful harmonic within it. It is the light that was in the heart of my cousin but here it is unfocussed and unimaginably vast. I rest in the Christ light, not passive but alive with wisdom, understanding and tolerance.

And now I understand.

I understand.

After death.
Darkness. My life is over. I am in the tomb under our house, where Yeshua lay and where my body was laid. I can see the light of my body with that of my son Japheth next to it. He is with me now, he clings to me; the passage of death has mercifully left love undimmed but he cannot understand and I am trying to explain to him. There is a radiance from the other resting-place in the tomb where Yeshua's body was laid which has a deep peace within it. I can feel Japheth's understanding grow as he feels it too.

As his understanding grows, mine grows too. Behind

my actions was one simple truth: I could not bear the loss. I cannot blame myself for what I did. It was an act of self-destruction but it was born of love – are not all such acts?

A deep compassion begins to grow within me, a self-understanding that is generated not from the radiance of my cousin but from within my self. It is a compassion that is not limited to my self either because it enables me to see all humanity in a similar light. We are all born of love; we come from love and we return to love, and all that passes between is an attempt to understand love, for love is the lesson of life, and the lessons of love are hard.

I am alone. Japheth has moved away now. It is a comfortable aloneness, although not without distress. I am contemplating the events that led me to this place, and am having to accept the unpalatable fact that it may have been better had I lived. Letting go of life was a hope born of desperation and now, despite my experience in the tomb, the feeling of having failed leads me to question everything. I am not sure what it all meant, what was real or whether my life was worth anything.

I can see Ruth from this place; she is numb with shock, a shock that transforms to grief and rage at what has happened. She lives in a world of unending torment. Perhaps she bears the suffering that I could not.

Josephes' death was not premeditated.
My death was not premeditated nor was it difficult or painful. When I entered the water that day it was not with the intention of ending my life. I had considered the option, of course, but up to that point had not chosen it. What happened was that when I slipped and went under, a door opened, that was all, a door opened and I let go and went through it.

It was the pain that I could not bear, the pain that I submerged in the Sea of Galilee. Sweet freedom, the cessation of suffering, the desire to rest in peace, were in that moment more powerful and attractive to me than anything that life could possibly offer. It was hardly even a conscious choice, I just wanted some relief, some peace.

A healing.
My absorption in these deliberations is interrupted by the awareness of a soft grey light, like the early light of dawn. Very gradually the intensity increases, the grey turns to white and then the concentration and depth grows. I cannot look directly at it, the energy is too great. As it reaches fullness I have to turn my back on it until I can barely glimpse at it from the corner of my eye. It is quite unlike any light I have ever seen or felt in my life. It has an unsurpassed purity; but it is not just light, it is alive, absolutely full of love and of understanding and intelligence. Within its beams and threads is everything that has ever been or can ever be, there is nothing within it that is not perfect.

From within this radiance steps Yeshua. He walks towards me and sits down beside me, his form protecting me from the brilliance. No words pass between us but I begin to understand. I understand the part I played, the part that we all played. A great scheme that stretches back and forward into infinity unrolls before me and I know that Yeshua is helping me to glimpse the heart of God. It heals, it brings peace. This light is the source, it is why Yeshua came, it is from where he comes. He comes from light and he will return to light. As will we all.

The peace and the understanding.
I look back over the crucifixion, and I see my despair and my anger in a different perspective now. I see what might have been had I not drowned: continuing the work, managing the estate in Cyprus, caring for the family, perhaps visiting my father in Britain by sea, getting to know my half-sister, Mary Magdalene, and bringing news and supplies.

I feel the regret, a sense of having let the family and my cousin down but I also feel the peace and understanding in this place, the attention and concern of others here who come to offer help. There are conversations with my cousin, where so much is accepted and understood. There is no fear here, no anger and no anguish; there is knowing and wisdom.

My part has been played. I feel the gratitude of the man I loved more than life. It is a healing in every sense of the word and now I am able to watch over those I love and commune with the light of each one, making my peace with my father and my wife and knowing that I will be reunited with each.

Now I know that nothing is ever truly lost in death; it just becomes clearer, greater in understanding and exalted.

The author's view of the Memories of Josephes

As you have read these memories I imagine that you will often have had cause to question the truth and accuracy of what I have presented. I do not blame you. I have questioned the validity of these words from the moment I started to write them down.

I cannot offer any evidence to support them, but on the other hand I know that they are not entirely a figment of my imagination. In fact, I was raised in a firmly anti-religious household and my knowledge of the Bible is scant. This has not prevented the vivid but fleeting images and feelings impinging on my meditations.

It is these images that have given rise to the writings, similar to those that Wellesley Tudor-Pole in his book 'A Man Seen Afar' referred to as 'glimpses'. As I meditated I would often begin to feel quite intense emotions or sensations. For example at the time I recalled Josephes' beating at the hands of the Romans I felt like crying and the skin on my back felt tight and sore for two days. The images were not simply visual; when they came I found that I could 'enter' them and re-experience what Josephes was seeing, thinking and feeling. I would then describe the scene and the feelings in writing.

Many of the memories have been confirmed as being true by a channelled source, Joseph of Arimathea (the Master), but this will hardly satisfy the sceptic. On the other hand the turn of phrase is not entirely my own, and from time to time neither is the wisdom that is expressed in the words. Personally I believe that they are a merging of ancient memory and present reality; they contain an essence of truth.

It may seem glamorous to participate in a phenomenon such as this and I cannot deny that in many ways it is, especially when the memories are of relationships with such apparently hallowed personalities, but the memories are not selective. As well as remembering the beauty and loyalty of Josephes there have also been his human failings and limitations to recall: his anger, bitterness, envy and despair. I have also had to struggle with my belief. In this life I do not consider myself to have any particular spiritual acumen, unless this capacity for memory is it. I see myself as an ordinary man with fairly ordinary aspirations.

As I have recalled Josephes' life and his cares there have been times when the degree of intimacy and honesty have been almost intolerable. He has revealed more of his soul to me than I suspect I dare to know of my own. From time to time this has caused me to put down my pen and turn away. What has made me return, what has kept me going, is the capacity of some of the memories to touch my heart very deeply, something that they have consistently done. Whether or not they are true, it is this ability that makes them worthwhile to me. I hope that they have touched you as they have touched me.

Postscript

One thing that has always bothered me from early on in the writings is why, if Josephes knew of his cousin's fate and even met him after his death, did he take the loss so hard when it happened? When the manuscript was complete I put this question, through a deep-trance channel, to his father, the Master.

David: *'Something that has always puzzled me is that you have said in the past that Yeshua confided the foreknowledge of his death to three people: his uncle, his mother and his cousin, Josephes. I have never been able to understand why, if Josephes knew about his early demise, his reaction was so very extreme.'*

Master: *'Pre-knowledge of something taking place and acceptance of that event are two very different circumstances. Most people, we feel, when actually presented with fact – but not even all the facts, the clear facts – would take the impression that not sufficient had been done to remove Yeshua from those circumstances. We can well understand Josephes' rage, his anger that in the short time of a few days a vibrant man can be reduced to one crucified like a common thief. Our own awareness is not particularly that the subject of his ultimate death would have been discussed a great deal. It would have been more generality, his awareness, not of the mode of death but of dying for his beliefs, dying for that which had been entrusted to him to spread to mankind. So it is more than possible that your equation of his acceptance of dying for his beliefs was quite different from being betrayed, flogged and crucified.'*

I continue to meditate daily and as time has passed Josephes comes less frequently. I am now writing the thoughts and words of a man called Malachi who was the great-grandson of Abraham. When Malachi first made himself known to me he spoke the following words:

'Josephes was a very, very fortunate man; he did not have to spend hours and hours and hours of time in meditation, supplication and prayer to find the Christ. Christ was his companion, his friend, they walked together, they talked, they loved one another deeply. My son, there are many, many in spirit and in life who would have given anything to have been in that position. We say this to you because although we are aware that you appreciate him very deeply, that you have no intention of losing touch with him, there is always the danger when a new teacher steps forward that those who have served in the past are relegated to a back shelf. Josephes brings knowledge of the Christ. Believe us when we say that there is no greater gift that those in Spirit can bring.'

And Japheth?
Many of the personalities who were members of Josephes' family and friends at the time of Christ are living at this

time. From among these a diverse group who were involved in the drama of Yeshua's life have formed. The purpose of this group is to play a part in the dawn of the Golden Age and to help the Children of Light establish themselves in life. (The Children of Light are souls who have no karmic need to be re-born, they have already finished their earthly journey. They are choosing incarnation at this time to help humanity initiate the much-needed changes in our societies and in our ways of thinking and acting. They are the harbingers of the Golden Age. The eldest are now in their mid-teens.)

As I have written down these memories and the events of that time have emerged I have often wondered what became of Japheth. In all other cases the identities of the personalities involved were revealed through contact with Joseph of Arimathea via his channel. One year ago, in response to a direct question, he revealed that in this life Japheth is a woman: the mother of our sons and my wife of twenty-three years.

David Davidson, Summer 1997.

How the soul remembers the past

It is an intriguing question as to how in the present time David can remember the events that happened to Josephes 2000 years ago. Before discussing this, it may be useful to give first a brief explanation of the nature of the soul and reincarnation. It is not too surprising that the nature of soul is quite complex and the following is but a brief exposition. The source of the explanation is the Master.

Initially soul was one vast energy field. At a particular point in evolution this exploded into a myriad of particles which gathered together into Higher Selves. The Master has often said that it is difficult to explain the true nature of the Higher Self. Language itself is based on what individuals see around them, and it is difficult to understand what cannot be perceived.

Each individual soul, therefore, is an aspect or particle of a Higher Self and each Higher Self contains more particles than there are cells in a human body. Not all aspects incarnate, just as a woman has the potential to conceive hundreds of children in a lifetime and may only actually give birth to two or three children.

If the Higher Self could be seen it would resemble a vast rainbow, and the particles that comprise it are organised according to the colours of that rainbow which are called light streams – pink, orange, amethyst, gold, silver, green and blue and all the hundreds of shades in between. Each light stream has a different learning pattern and this pattern takes an average of two to three hundred incarnations to fulfil. David and Josephes are both from the same light stream, the golden one, which was also the light stream of Yeshua.

We know from basic physics that these different colours are simply another way of saying that the light streams are different streams of energy vibrating at different frequencies. (The violet end of our visual spectrum vibrates faster than the red end.)

Apparently if one could see the Higher Self one would be delighted by its great beauty. The Master has said:

'Imagine looking at a sunset, how the sky above radiates the light, how each cloud represents a facet of the pinks and oranges, the blues and greens of the sunset; and then imagine the Higher Self.

'Some may say, but if the soul has such proportions how is there room for so many in spirit? But spirit is not measured by an area of space; spirit is a dimension. It is not like your world where you must travel from one place to another in order to experience the change of view, the different countries and the people dwelling in them. Spirit being a dimension of light contains all things in a comparatively small area in comparison to your world. Unfortunately to be able to visualise that which you have never seen is virtually impossible.'

So a true insight into the Higher Self – the total soul – can never be achieved because it is of a vastly different vibration from that of which the body is aware.

The soul has the opportunity to learn in spirit as well as upon the earth, but the earth is an important school for the soul, where the Higher Self can enrich its understanding with first-hand knowledge of the full range of human emotions. Ultimately it is where the Higher Self can come to know love. It is the planet where the soul can express itself, can move forward and has that greatest blessing of all – free will. The soul in its own environment does not have free will. It has total knowledge and understanding of life and universal law; it has accepted what it is simply to be, but that is not sufficient for true learning.

Existence is not confined to one life, to that which is being appreciated at the present time; existence is continuous. At the end of each life the soul returns to spirit, rejoins the Higher Self and cannot incarnate again. The knowledge gained from that life is then shared among all the aspects of the Higher Self and enriches it, and so that which transpired within that life is now in the full consciousness of the entire Higher Self and therefore also within that fragment of soul within us when we are next on earth. The truths which come with each lifetime remain within the soul. The Higher Self is a culmination of all lives, all awareness, all truths, all knowledge that has been gained by accepting the world as it is while that soul journeyed through time.

However when the soul enters the physical self at the time of birth, conscious knowledge of the past is concealed. From time to time throughout the life certain fragments are remembered through synchronicity, experiences of déjà vu or dreaming. These often come at times when the personality needs a little help to go forward, to develop and succeed and to allow the spirituality to evolve; another way that this memory can be facilitated is through the practice of meditation.

How David remembered the past.

During the writing of these memories David often had cause to doubt the authenticity of what he was writing. He shared this with the Master who explained to him a little of the nature of the mechanism that has enabled him to write the memories of Josephes.

Master: *'You are not writing in the way that some mediums do, by closing the eyes and allowing the hand to write unbidden; it is a more clarified way of writing. You are receiving this understanding in a very pure way but it is not a memory of your life at this time but a memory of Josephes' life at that time. You feel that you share this memory because you are both of the same Higher Self.*

'The complexity of these teachings is not made any easier by the fact that you live in a completely different time of reality

within the world. He is sending a light pattern through space and time which amalgamates with your reception. It is not necessary for him to be aware of the present time in which you live, but you are being made aware of the time when he did because soul has a collective memory. You have a greater understanding of what took place, so virtually it is his memory that you are writing down.'

David therefore feels that these memories of Josephes' life of 2000 years ago are not the results of what is known as channelling, nor yet automatic writing, but are a form of past-life memory.

Peter Wheeler

Genealogical Charts

The House of David

This genealogical table clearly shows the relationship between Jesus, John the Baptist and Joseph of Arimathea, all descended from the line of David.

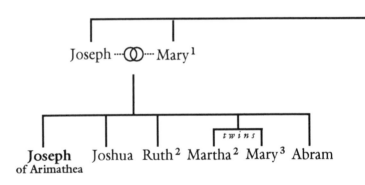

1 *The three half sisters bore the name of 'Mary' (a common Jewish name) linked to the family name of their respective fathers, for their mother had had three husbands.*

2 *Died in childhood*

3 *Still born*

4 *Died in infancy*

5 *Sex unknown*

House of David

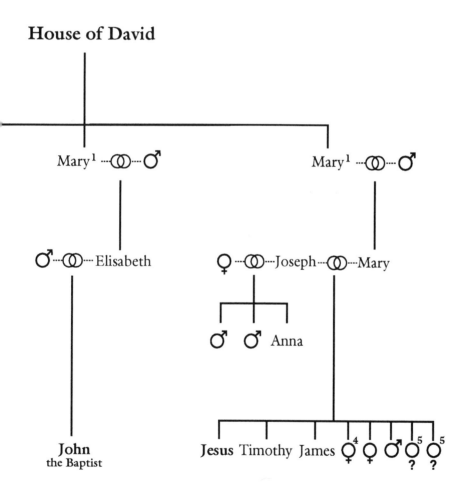

Joseph of Arimathea's Family

1 *Non-Jewish*

2 *Died within a few months*

3 *Died soon after birth*

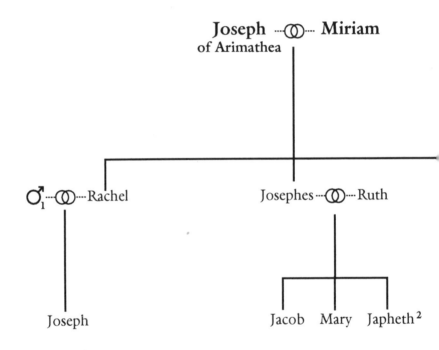

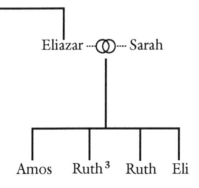

The extended family of Joseph of Arimathea

1 *Died at 1 week*

2 *Died at age 12*

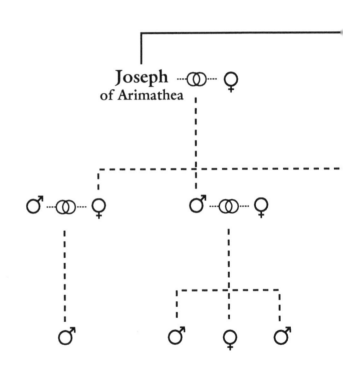

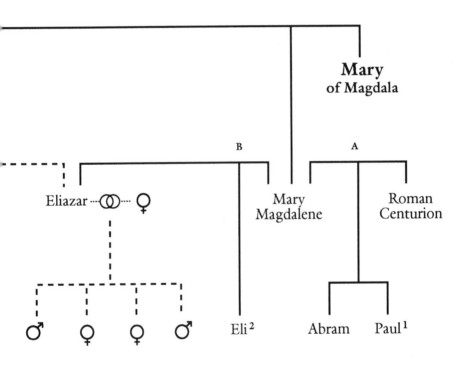

The Memories of Josephes
Soul Memories of a Cousin of Jesus

This book is made up of the memories of
Josephes, the eldest son of Joseph of
Arimathea. During meditation David Davidson
began to see vivid glimpses of the life and
times of Josephes, who lived 2000 years ago in
Jerusalem and Cyprus. What makes these
memories special is that Josephes was a cousin
of Yeshua (Jesus) who was his constant boyhood
companion and lifelong confidant.

Over the course of three and a half years the
story of Josephes' life emerged, chronicling
his struggles, his intense relationship with his
cousin and his own ultimate death.

This book presents a beautiful, poetic and at
times, dramatic account, not just of the life of
Josephes but also of the trials of Yeshua as he
grew, realised, and fulfilled his destiny.